高一同學的自標

- 1. 熟背「高中常用7000字」
- 2. 月期考得高分
- 3. 會說流利的英語

1. 「用會話背7000字①」書＋CD　280元

以三個極短句為一組的方式，讓同學背了會話，同時快速增加單字。高一同學要從「國中常用2000字」挑戰「高中常用7000字」，加強單字是第一目標。

2. 「一分鐘背9個單字」書＋CD　280元

利用字首、字尾的排列，讓你快速增加單字。一次背9個比背1個字簡單。

3. rival

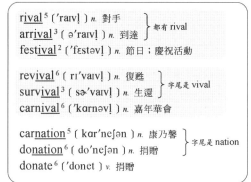

| rival⁵ (ˈraɪvl̩) n. 對手 |
| arrival³ (əˈraɪvl̩) n. 到達 | 都有 rival |
| festival² (ˈfɛstəvl̩) n. 節日；慶祝活動 |

| revival⁶ (rɪˈvaɪvl̩) n. 復甦 |
| survival³ (səˈvaɪvl̩) n. 生還 | 字尾是 vival |
| carnival⁶ (ˈkɑrnəvl̩) n. 嘉年華會 |

| carnation⁵ (kɑrˈneʃən) n. 康乃馨 |
| donation⁶ (doˈneʃən) n. 捐贈 | 字尾是 nation |
| donate⁶ (ˈdonet) v. 捐贈 |

3. 「一口氣考試英語」書＋CD　280元

把大學入學考試題目編成會話，背了以後，會說英語，又會考試。

例如：

What a nice surprise!（真令人驚喜！）【常考】
I can't believe my eyes.
（我無法相信我的眼睛。）
Little did I dream of seeing you here.
（做夢也沒想到會在這裡看到你。）【駒澤大】

4.「一口氣背文法」書+ CD 280元
英文文法範圍無限大，規則無限多，誰背得完？
劉毅老師把文法整體的概念，編成216句，背完
了會做文法題、會說英語，也會寫作文。既是一
本文法書，也是一本會話書。

1. 現在簡單式的用法

I *get up* early every day.	我每天早起。
I *understand* this rule now.	我現在了解這條規定了。
Actions *speak* louder than words.	行動勝於言辭。

【二、三句強調實踐早起】

5.「高中英語聽力測驗①」書+ MP3 280元
6.「高中英語聽力測驗進階」書+ MP3 280元
高一月期考聽力佔20%，我們根據大考中心公布的
聽力題型編輯而成。

7.「高一月期考英文試題」書 280元
收集建中、北一女、師大附中、中山、成功、景
美女中等各校試題，並聘請各校名師編寫模擬試
題。

8.「高一英文克漏字測驗」書 180元

9.「高一英文閱讀測驗」書 180元
全部取材自高一月期考試題，英雄
所見略同，重複出現的機率很高。
附有翻譯及詳解，不必查字典，對
錯答案都有明確交待，做完題目，
一看就懂。

高二同學的目標──提早準備考大學

1.「用會話背7000字①②」
   書+CD，每冊280元

「用會話背7000字」能夠解決
所有學英文的困難。高二同學
可先從第一冊開始背，第一冊
和第二冊沒有程度上的差異，
背得越多，單字量越多，在腦
海中的短句越多。每一個極短句大多不超過5個字，1個字或
2個字都可以成一個句子，如：「用會話背7000字①」p.184，
每一句都2個字，好背得不得了，而且與生活息息相關，是
每個人都必須知道的知識，例如：成功的祕訣是什麼？

11. What are the keys to success?

Be *ambitious*.	要有<u>雄心</u>。
Be *confident*.	要有<u>信心</u>。
Have *determination*.	要有<u>決心</u>。
Be *patient*.	要有<u>耐心</u>。
Be *persistent*.	要有<u>恆心</u>。
Show *sincerity*.	要有<u>誠心</u>。
Be *charitable*.	要有<u>愛心</u>。
Be *modest*.	要<u>虛心</u>。
Have *devotion*.	要<u>專心</u>。

當你背單字的時候，就要有「雄心」，要「決心」背好，對
自己要有「信心」，一定要有「耐心」和「恆心」，背書時
要「專心」。

背完後，腦中有2,160個句子，那不得了，無限多的排列組
合，可以寫作文。有了單字，翻譯、閱讀測驗、克漏字都難
不倒你了。高二的時候，要下定決心，把7000字背熟、背
爛。雖然高中課本以7000字為範圍，編書者為了便宜行事，
往往超出7000字，同學背了少用的單字，反倒忽略真正重要
的單字。千萬記住，背就要背「高中常用7000字」，背完之
後，天不怕、地不怕，任何考試都難不倒你。

2.「時速破百單字快速記憶」書 250元

字尾是 try，重音在倒數第三音節上

entry³ (ˈɛntrɪ) n. 進入【No entry. 禁止進入。】
country¹ (ˈkʌntrɪ) n. 國家；鄉下【ou 讀 /ʌ/，為例外字】
ministry⁴ (ˈmɪnɪstrɪ) n. 部【mini = small】

chemistry⁴ (ˈkɛmɪstrɪ) n. 化學
geometry⁵ (dʒɪˈɑmətrɪ) n. 幾何學【geo 土地，metry 測量】
industry² (ˈɪndəstrɪ) n. 工業；勤勉【這個字重音常唸錯】

poetry¹ (ˈpo‧ɪtrɪ) n. 詩
poultry⁴ (ˈpoltrɪ) n. 家禽 ⎱ 字尾 y 表「集合名詞」
pastry⁵ (ˈpestrɪ) n. 糕餅

3.「高二英文克漏字測驗」書 180元

4.「高二英文閱讀測驗」書 180元
全部選自各校高二月期考試題精華，英雄所見略
同，再出現的機率很高。

5.「7000字學測試題詳解」書 250元
一般模考題為了便宜行事，往往超出7000字範圍
，無論做多少份試題，仍然有大量生字，無法進
步。唯有鎖定7000字為範圍的試題，才會對準備
考試有幫助。每份試題都經「劉毅英文」同學實
際考過，效果奇佳。附有詳細解答，單字標明級
數，對錯答案都有明確交待，不需要再查字典，
做完題目，再看詳解，快樂無比。

6.「高中常用7000字解析【豪華版】」書 390元
按照「大考中心高中英文參考詞彙表」編輯而成
。難背的單字有「記憶技巧」、「同義字」及
「反義字」，關鍵的單字有「典型考題」。大學
入學考試核心單字，以紅色標記。

7.「高中7000字測驗題庫」書 180元
取材自大規模考試，解答詳盡，節省查字典的時間。

唸一字金，變成超人！

　　人生最大的浪費，不是錢，而是時間。很多人為了學英文，浪費了太多寶貴的時間，沒有獲得快樂，反而帶來痛苦和絕望。這是全世界所有學英文者的共同問題。

　　想了 50 年，才想到如何利用右腦長期記憶的原理，發明了「**英文一字金**」。我每天早上在公園，一面散步，一面背「成功勵志經」，真是快樂無比。

例如：

背三句話就有感覺
- *Attend*.（要參加。）
- *Adjust*.（要調整。）
- *Adapt*.（要適應。）

再背三句感觸更深
- *Achieve*.（要達成目標。）
- *Accomplish*.（要完成任務。）
- *Accumulate*.（要累積。）

連續背九句，背至 5 秒內，你會感覺到想飛了！
- Be *active*.（要有活力。）
- *Acute*.（要敏銳。）
- *Aggressive*.（要有衝勁。）

背「成功勵志經」的時候，**無形中被洗腦**，從此，我把握每一次參加（attend）活動的機會，我學會調整（adjust）自己，學會適應（adapt）新的環境。

　　「成功勵志經」裡面教你，要達到（achieve）目標，做事情不要做一半，要一件、一件地完成（accomplish），**不斷累積（accumulate）**知識和經驗，感覺到永遠不會老。

我今年 73 歲，不想回到 72 歲，因為還沒有發明「英文一字金」；不想回到二、三十歲，因為沒有比現在有錢，沒有比現在快樂。累積的力量讓我一直勇往直前。

我在公園裡，一面運動、一面背，嘴裡唸唸有辭，變得很有活力（active），腦筋很敏銳（acute），衝勁十足（aggressive）。一天一天進步，每天都有成就感。

太可怕了！背 9 個字就有這樣的感覺，當你每天背 216 個字的時候，像是上帝在指引你，走向一條通往成功的大道，你會有一種衝動，急著想要把這個方法傳出去，拯救受苦受難學英文的人。

我在深圳「邦德教育」給 150 位英文老師師訓時，感覺不像是在上課，像是在傳達福音。英文老師的潛力被激發，立刻感覺到對未來有了希望。他們的表現，反射到我身上，我像是被閃電打到，變成超人，連續上 3 小時的課，一點都不覺得累，還很興奮，有用不完的體力。難怪有人會拋棄家庭，出家修行，他們說唸經最快樂，沒有煩惱。

「英文一字金」會讓老師越教越喜歡教，因為教學相長，你自己的英文也在進步。即使只有一個學生，老師也喜歡上，因為有人陪你一起背。天天唸「英文一字金」，不只是百毒不侵，沒有煩惱，更像是自己正在充電。一旦教書，所有的電都釋放出來了。相信「英文一字金」不只能夠解決人類學英文的困難，而且還能激勵人心，朝成功的目標前進。

劉毅

How to Succeed

1. A

看英文唸出中文	一口氣說九句	看中文唸出英文
attend[2] 〔 ə'tɛnd 〕v.	**Attend**. 要參加。	參加
adjust[4] 〔 ə'dʒʌst 〕v.	**Adjust**. 要調整。	調整
adapt[4] 〔 ə'dæpt 〕v.	**Adapt**. 要適應。	適應

字首是 Ad

achieve[3] 〔 ə'tʃiv 〕v.	**Achieve**. 要達成。	達成
accomplish[4] 〔 ə'kɑmplɪʃ 〕v.	**Accomplish**. 要完成。	完成
accumulate[6] 〔 ə'kjumjə‚let 〕v.	**Accumulate**. 要累積。	累積

字首都是 Ac

active[2] 〔'æktɪv 〕adj.	Be **active**. 要有活力。	活躍的；主動的
acute[6] 〔 ə'kjut 〕adj.	**Acute**. 要敏銳。	敏銳的
aggressive[4] 〔 ə'grɛsɪv 〕adj.	**Aggressive**. 要有衝勁。	侵略的；積極的

字首是 ac

I. 背景說明：

　　Attend.（要參加。） 要成功，什麼都要儘量參加。*Attend* every meeting.（每一次會議都要參加。）*Attend* every event.（每個活動都要參加。）*Attend* every training session.（每次的訓練課程都要參加。）*Adjust*.（要調整。）可說成：Be willing to *adjust*.（要願意調整。）*Adjust* your outlook.（要調整你的看法。）adjust 作「調整」解時，就是「改變」（＝*change*）。*Adapt*.（要適應。）可說成：*Adapt* to change.（要適應改變。）*Adapt* to the situation.（要適應情況。）*Adapt* to the environment.（要適應環境。）

　　Achieve.（要達成。）可說成：*Achieve* your goals.（要達成你的目標。）Let nothing stop you from *achieving* success.（不要讓任何事阻止你獲得成功。）*Accomplish*.（要完成。）可說成：*Accomplish* every task.（要完成每一項任務。）Don't rest until you *accomplish* the mission.（要直到完成任務才休息。）

> achieve（達成）和 accomplish（完成）的區別：
> *Achieve* the goal.（要達成目標。）
> *Accomplish* the task.（要完成任務。）

Accumulate.（要累積。）可說成：*Accumulate* skills and knowledge.（要累積技能和知識。）*Accumulate* experience.（要累積經驗。）當一項任務完成後，再完成一個，就能累積成就。（*Accumulate achievements*.）

　　Be active.（要有活力。）可說成：Stay *active* in your field.（在你的領域中要保持活躍。）Play an *active* role at work.（在工作中要扮演積極的角色。）*Acute.*（要敏銳。）（= *Be acute.* = *Be sharp.*）可說成：Develop an *acute* sense of business.（要培養對事業的敏銳感。）Have an *acute* mind.（頭腦要敏銳。）*Aggressive.*（要有攻擊性；要積極進取；要有衝勁；要有企圖心。）（= *Be aggressive.*）可說成：Be *aggressive* when necessary.（有必要時，要積極爭取。）Take an *aggressive* approach to problem-solving.（要採取積極的方法解決問題。）

　　每回九句背完後，可發表一篇演講，來激勵你周圍的人。

Ladies and gentlemen:

Attend.
Adjust.
Adapt.

Achieve.
Accomplish.
Accumulate.

Be active.
Acute.
Aggressive.

Then you will succeed.

II. 短篇英語演講：

Ladies and gentlemen: 各位先生，各位女士：

Attend every meeting. 每一次會議都要參加。
Adjust your outlook. 要調整你的看法。
Adapt to change. 要適應改變。

Achieve your goals. 要達成你的目標。
Accomplish every task. 要完成每一項任務。
Accumulate experience. 要累積經驗。

Be active at work. 工作時要積極。
Have an *acute* mind. 頭腦要敏銳。
Take an *aggressive* approach to problem-solving.
要採取積極的方法解決問題。

Then you will succeed. 那麼你就會成功。

III. 短篇作文：
How to Succeed

In order to succeed, you must *attend* every event. You must be willing to *adjust* and *adapt* to new situations. Let nothing stop you from *achieving* your goals. Don't rest until you *accomplish* the mission. *Moreover*, it's important to *accumulate* skills and knowledge. *Be active* in your field and develop an *acute* sense of business. *Most importantly*, be *aggressive* when necessary.

如何成功

　　爲了要成功，你每個活動都必須參加。你必須願意調整，並適應新的情況。不要讓任何事阻止你達成目標。要直到完成任務才休息。此外，累積技能和知識非常重要。在你的領域中要很活躍，並培養對事業的敏銳感。最重要的是，有必要時，要積極爭取。

IV. 填空：

　　To be successful, you must ___1___ every meeting, appointment and social event. You must be willing to ___2___ your outlook to the changing times. A successful person must learn to ___3___ to new environments.

　　In the meantime, you must focus on ___4___ your goals and ___5___ your tasks. You can ___6___ the experience you need to succeed.

　　What's more, you must stay ___7___ in your field. You will develop an ___8___ sense of business. Usually successful people are ___9___ but only when necessary.

　　爲了要成功，你必須每一場會議、約會，和社交活動都要參加。你必須願意根據時代的改變，來調整你的看法。成功的人必須學習適應新環境。

　　同時，你必須專注於達成你的目標，及完成你的任務。你可以累積成功所需的經驗。

　　此外，你必須在你的領域中保持活躍。你會培養出對事業的敏銳感。通常成功的人會積極爭取，不過只在有必要的時候。

【解答】1. attend　2. adjust　3. adapt　4. achieving
　　　　5. accomplishing　6. accumulate　7. active　8. acute
　　　　9. aggressive

V. 詞彙題：

Directions: *Choose the one word that best completes the sentence.*

1. It's important to _____ every meeting.
   (A) attain (B) astonish (C) assure (D) attend

2. You must _____ your outlook to achieve success.
   (A) attack (B) attract (C) adjust (D) awake

3. Try to _____ to your new environment as quickly as you can.
   (A) authorize (B) adapt (C) award (D) assist

4. Believe that you can _____ anything you want.
   (A) achieve (B) appeal (C) arise (D) appear

5. Don't stop or give up until you _____ your goal.
   (A) alternate (B) anticipate (C) accomplish (D) apologize

6. _____ skills and knowledge to increase your value.
   (A) Accelerate (B) Accumulate (C) Arrest (D) Argue

7. Be an _____ participant in life, not a spectator.
   (A) allergic (B) accidental (C) absent (D) active

8. Have an _____ sense of right and wrong.
   (A) acute (B) ancient (C) anonymous (D) approximate

9. Take an _____ approach to business and work hard.
   (A) artificial (B) athletic (C) awkward (D) aggressive

【答案】1.（D）　2.（C）　3.（B）　4.（A）　5.（C）　6.（B）
　　　　7.（D）　8.（A）　9.（D）

VI. 同義字整理：

1. **attend** 〔 ə'tɛnd 〕 v. 參加
   - = be present
   - = appear at
   - = put in an appearance at

2. **adjust** 〔 ə'dʒʌst 〕 v. 調整
   - = change 〔 tʃendʒ 〕
   - = alter 〔 'ɔltɚ 〕
   - = modify 〔 'madə,faɪ 〕

3. **adapt** 〔 ə'dæpt 〕 v. 適應
   - = accustom 〔 ə'kʌstəm 〕
   - = reconcile 〔 'rɛkən,saɪl 〕
   - = accommodate 〔 ə'kamə,det 〕

4. **achieve** 〔 ə'tʃiv 〕 v. 達成
   - = accomplish 〔 ə'kamplɪʃ 〕
   - = attain 〔 ə'ten 〕
   - = reach 〔 ritʃ 〕
   - = realize 〔 'riə,laɪz 〕

5. **accomplish** 〔 ə'kamplɪʃ 〕 v. 完成
   - = finish 〔 'fɪnɪʃ 〕
   - = complete 〔 kəm'plit 〕
   - = carry out

6. **accumulate** 〔 ə'kjumjə,let 〕 v. 累積
   - = build up
   - = increase 〔 ɪn'kris 〕
   - = collect 〔 kə'lɛkt 〕

7. **active** 〔'æktɪv 〕 adj. 活躍的；主動的
   - = busy 〔 'bɪzɪ 〕
   - = involved 〔 ɪn'valvd 〕
   - = energetic 〔,ɛnɚ'dʒɛtɪk 〕

8. **acute** 〔 ə'kjut 〕 adj. 敏銳的
   - = perceptive 〔 pɚ'sɛptɪv 〕
   - = sharp 〔 ʃarp 〕
   - = insightful 〔 'ɪn,saɪtfəl 〕

9. **aggressive** 〔 ə'grɛsɪv 〕 adj. 侵略的；積極的
   - = forceful 〔 'forsfəl 〕
   - = powerful 〔 'pauɚfəl 〕
   - = vigorous 〔 'vɪgərəs 〕

How to Succeed

2. B

看英文唸出中文	一 口 氣 説 九 句	看中文唸出英文
bear[2,1]〔 bɛr 〕v.	**Bear**. 要勇於承擔。	忍受;承擔
bloom[4]〔 blum 〕v.	**Bloom**. 要發光、發亮。	開花;發展
blunt[6]〔 blʌnt 〕adj.	Be **blunt**. 說話要直率。	鈍的;直率的

兩短一長 / 都是 bl 開頭

beware[5]〔 bɪ'wɛr 〕v.	**Beware**. 要小心。	小心
benefit[3]〔 'bɛnəfɪt 〕v.	**Benefit**. 要獲益。	獲益;獲利
believe[1]〔 bɪ'liv 〕v.	**Believe** in yourself. 要相信自己的能力。	相信

都是 Be 開頭

break[1]〔 brek 〕v.	**Break** through. 要突破。	打破
brilliant[3]〔 'brɪljənt 〕adj.	Be **brilliant**. 要發出光芒。	燦爛的;聰明的
broaden[5]〔 'brɔdn̩ 〕v.	**Broaden** your horizons. 要拓展眼界。	加寬;拓展

都是 br 開頭

I. 背景說明：

Bear.（要勇於承擔。）bear 有三個意思：①忍受②承受③生（小孩）。可說成：*Bear* the responsibility.（要承擔責任。）*Bear* the burden.（要承受負擔。）*Bloom*.（要發光、發亮。）bloom 的主要意思是「開花」，在這裡引申為「發光；發亮；發展」(＝*develop*)。可說成：Let your talent *bloom*.（要發揮你的才能。）*Bloom* like a flower.（要像花一樣盛開。）*Be blunt*.（要直率。）blunt 的意思有「鈍的；不鋒利的；直率的；直言不諱的」，「直率的」人就像「鈍的」刀子一樣，傻里傻氣的。可說成：*Be blunt* with people.（對人要直率。）(＝*Be straightforward with people.*)

Beware.（要小心。）可說成：*Beware* of unseen dangers.（要小心看不見的危險。）*Beware* of dishonest people.（要小心不誠實的人。）*Benefit*.（要獲益。）可說成：*Benefit* from hard work.（要從辛苦工作中獲益。）*Benefit* from experience.（要從經驗中獲益。）*Believe in yourself*.（要相信你自己的能力。）*Believe* in what you are doing.（要相信你自己所做的事是正確的。）*believe* 和 *believe in* 的區別：believe 是「相信某人說的話」，believe in 是「信仰；信任；相信…的存在；相信…是好的」。*Believe in* your work.（要對你的工作有信心。）(＝*Have confidence in your work.*)

Break through.（要突破。）成功的人，要突破，要與眾不同。可説成：***Break through*** barriers.（要突破障礙。）***Break through*** mental limitations.（要突破心理的限制。）***Break through*** to the mainstream.（要突破成為主流。）（= *Reach the mainstream and become popular.*）***Be brilliant.***（要發出光芒。）brilliant 的主要意思是「燦爛的；光亮的」，引申為「聰明的；才華橫溢的；技藝高超的；傑出的；非常成功的」。可説成：Be sharp.（要聰明一點。）（= *Be clever.*）Be outstanding.（要傑出。）（= *Be great.* = *Be remarkable.* = *Be excellent.*）***Broaden your horizons.***（要拓展眼界。）（= *Extend the scope of your knowledge.* = *Widen the range of your experience.*）注意：horizon 的意思是「地平線」，horizons 才是「知識範圍」。所以，英文一定要背句子，少個 s 就不行。

Dear friends:

Bear.
Bloom.
Be blunt.

Beware.
Benefit.
Believe in yourself.

Break through.
Be brilliant.
Broaden your horizons.

Then success will follow you.

II. 短篇英語演講：

Dear friends: 親愛的朋友：

Bear the responsibility. 要承擔責任。
Bloom like a flower. 要像花一樣盛開。
Be blunt with people. 對人要直率。

Beware of unseen dangers. 要小心看不見的危險。
Benefit from hard work. 要從辛苦工作中獲益。
Believe in yourself. 要相信你自己的能力。

Break through barriers. 要突破障礙。
Be brilliant and witty. 要聰明而且風趣。
Broaden your horizons and enrich your life.
要拓展眼界，豐富你的生命。

Then success will follow you. 那樣你就會成功。

III. 短篇作文：

How to Achieve Success

Success comes when you *bear* the burden. At this time,
let your talent *bloom*. It helps to *be blunt* with people, but
don't hurt their feelings. *However*, you must *beware* of
dishonest people. By overcoming this hazard, you will *benefit*
from your experience. *Meanwhile, believe in yourself. Break*
through to the mainstream. *Be brilliant* and intelligent. *Above*
all, you must *broaden your horizons* and enrich your life.

如何成功

　　當你承受重擔，成功就會來到。這時候，要讓你的才能發光、發亮。對別人直率，但又不傷害他們的感情，是很有幫助的。然而，你必須小心不誠實的人。藉由克服這樣的危險，你會從經驗中獲益。同時，要相信你自己的能力。要突破成為主流。要傑出而且聰明。最重要的是，你必須拓展眼界，豐富你的生命。

IV. 填空：

　　Successful people ___1___ the responsibility of their actions, which in turn, allows them to ___2___ like a flower. They are ___3___ and straightforward with people but never unkind.

　　On the other hand, to succeed, you must ___4___ of unseen dangers. Ultimately, you will ___5___ from putting in the extra effort. Successful people ___6___ in themselves.

　　To succeed, you must have ___7___ ideas, which allows you to ___8___ to the mainstream and become popular. Most of all, only if you ___9___ your horizons can you achieve success.

　　成功的人會為自己的行為承擔責任，因而會讓他們像花一樣盛開。他們對人非常直率，但絕不會冷酷無情。

　　另一方面，為了要成功，你必須小心看不見的危險。最後，你會因為所投入的額外努力而獲益。成功的人會相信自己的能力。

　　為了要成功，你必須要有很聰明的想法，讓你能突破成為主流，變得受歡迎。最重要的是，唯有拓展眼界，你才能成功。

【**解答**】 1. bear　 2. bloom　 3. blunt　 4. beware　 5. benefit
　　　　　 6. believe　 7. brilliant　 8. break through　 9. broaden
　　　　* ultimately〔ˈʌltəmɪtlɪ〕 *adv.* 最後
　　　　　最後一句的 only 加上副詞子句放在句首時，主要子句的主詞與動詞須倒裝，寫成 can you achieve。

V. 詞彙題：

Directions: *Choose the one word that best completes the sentence.*

1. _____ the weight of your responsibility.
   (A) Bake   (B) Bear   (C) Behave   (D) Betray

2. Allow your talent to _____ like a flower.
   (A) bloom   (B) blink   (C) bleach   (D) bounce

3. Occasionally, you may need to be _____ with people.
   (A) beneficial   (B) blank   (C) brisk   (D) blunt

4. _____ of dangerous and risky situations.
   (A) Beat   (B) Bend   (C) Beware   (D) Besiege

5. Know that you will _____ from hard work.
   (A) breathe   (B) bombard   (C) blend   (D) benefit

6. _____ in what you are doing, and you will go far.
   (A) Believe   (B) Bruise   (C) Browse   (D) Belong

7. With effort, you can _____ through barriers.
   (A) build   (B) break   (C) bulge   (D) ban

8. Successful people come up with _____ ideas.
   (A) barren   (B) biological   (C) brilliant   (D) bony

9. _____ your range of experience in order to learn more.
   (A) Bore   (B) Broaden   (C) Blush   (D) Burst

【答案】 1.(B)   2.(A)   3.(D)   4.(C)   5.(D)   6.(A)
         7.(B)   8.(C)   9.(B)

VI. 同義字整理：

1. **bear** 〔 bɛr 〕 *v.* 承擔
    = support 〔 sə'port 〕
    = carry 〔'kærɪ 〕
    = endure 〔 ɪn'djʊr 〕

    = shoulder 〔'ʃoldɚ 〕
    = sustain 〔 sə'sten 〕

2. **bloom** 〔 blum 〕 *v.* 開花；發展
    = grow 〔 gro 〕
    = develop 〔 dɪ'vɛləp 〕
    = succeed 〔 sək'sid 〕

    = flourish 〔'flɝɪʃ 〕
    = thrive 〔 θraɪv 〕
    = prosper 〔'prɑspɚ 〕

3. **blunt** 〔 blʌnt 〕 *adj.* 直率的
    = frank 〔 fræŋk 〕
    = straightforward 〔ˌstret'fɔrwɚd 〕
    = outspoken 〔 aʊt'spokən 〕

4. **beware** 〔 bɪ'wɛr 〕 *v.* 小心
    = be careful
    = look out
    = watch out

    = be wary
    = be cautious

5. **benefit** 〔'bɛnəfɪt 〕 *v.* 獲益；獲利
    = profit from
    = gain from
    = make the most of

6. **believe in yourself**
    要相信自己的能力
    = have faith in yourself
    = have confidence in yourself

7. **break through** 突破
    = advance 〔 əd'væns 〕
    = clear an obstruction

8. **brilliant** 〔'brɪljənt 〕 *adj.* 聰明的
    = smart 〔 smɑrt 〕
    = clever 〔'klɛvɚ 〕
    = intelligent 〔 ɪn'tɛlədʒənt 〕

9. **broaden your horizons**
    要拓展眼界
    = expand your thinking
    = accumulate experience
    = learn new things

How to Succeed

3. **C (1)**

看英文唸出中文	一口氣説九句	看中文唸出英文
chase[1] 〔 tʃes 〕 *v.*	**Chase**. 要追求。	追求
cheer[3] 〔 tʃɪr 〕 *v.*	**Cheer**. 要鼓舞他人。	歡呼
cherish[4] 〔'tʃɛrɪʃ 〕 *v.*	**Cherish**. 要珍惜。	珍惜

字首都是 Ch

---

conquer[4] 〔'kɑŋkɚ 〕 *v.*	**Conquer**. 要克服。	征服;克服
confront[5] 〔 kən'frʌnt 〕 *v.*	**Confront**. 要勇於面對。	面對
contribute[4] 〔 kən'trɪbjʊt 〕 *v.*	**Contribute**. 要有貢獻。	貢獻

字首都是 Con

---

confident[3] 〔'kɑnfədənt 〕 *adj.*	Be **confident**. 要有信心。	有信心的
competent[6] 〔'kɑmpətənt 〕 *adj.*	**Competent**. 要能幹。	能幹的
competitive[4] 〔 kəm'pɛtətɪv 〕 *adj.*	**Competitive**. 競爭心要強。	好競爭的

字首是 Compet

I. 背景説明：

Chase. （要追求。）可説成：**Chase** your dreams.（要追求你的夢想。）**Chase** your success.（要追求你的成功。）（= Chase success.）**Cheer**. （要鼓舞他人。）可説成：**Cheer** others.（要鼓舞他人。）（= Encourage others.）**Cheer** when you win.（當你贏的時候要歡呼。） 英文一字多義，要看前後句意來判斷它的意思，cheer 可作「歡呼；喝采；使振奮」解，不要去背哪個動詞及物或不及物，背句子就對了。 Cherish.（要珍惜。）可説成：**Cherish** the present.（要珍惜現在。）**Cherish** your time.（要珍惜你的時間。）**Cherish** your progress.（要珍惜你的進步。）

Conquer.（要克服。）可説成：**Conquer** any fear.（要克服任何的恐懼。）Believe that you can **conquer** any difficulty.（要相信你能克服任何困難。）conquer 有「征服」和「克服」的意思。Confront.（要勇於面對。）可説成：**Confront** every obstacle.（要勇於面對每一個阻礙。）Don't be afraid to **confront** any tough issues.（不要害怕面對任何困難的問題。）Contribute.（要有貢獻。）可説成：**Contribute** to the conversation.（要參與對話。）（= Have something to say.）有些人沈默寡言，無法當領袖。（Failures don't contribute to the conversation.）**Contribute** as much as you can.（要盡量貢獻。）**Contribute** your best effort.（要貢獻你最大的努力。）

　　Be confident.（要有信心。）可説成：Stand up straight and be *confident.*（挺直腰桿，要有信心。）A *confident* person can gain respect.（有信心的人才能獲得尊重。）*Competent.*（要能幹。）(=*Be competent.*) 可説成：Show others you are *competent.*（要讓別人知道你很能幹。）Be a *competent* employee.（要做個能幹的員工。）*Competitive.*（競爭心要強。）(= *Be competitive.*) Have a *competitive* spirit.（要有競爭的精神。）Be a *competitive* person.（要做個競爭心強的人。）competitive 的意思有：①競爭的②好競爭的③競爭激烈的。

　　用「英文一字金」可編成短篇和長篇演講。

> **Dear ladies and gentlemen:**
>
> Chase.
> Cheer.
> Cherish.
>
> Conquer.
> Confront.
> Contribute.
>
> Be confident.
> Competent.
> Competitive.
>
> **You will achieve success.**

II. 短篇英語演講：

Dear ladies and gentlemen: 親愛的各位先生、各位女士：

Chase your dreams. 要追求你的夢想。
Cheer others. 要鼓舞他人。
Cherish the present. 要珍惜現在。

Conquer any fear. 要克服任何的恐懼。
Confront every obstacle. 要勇於面對每一個阻礙。
Contribute your best effort. 要貢獻你最大的努力。

Stand up straight and *be confident*.
挺直腰桿，要有信心。
Be *competent*. 要能幹。
Be a *competitive* person. 要做個競爭心強的人。

You will achieve success. 你會成功的。

III. 短篇作文：

How to Be Successful

To achieve success, you first must *chase* your dreams. *Cheer* when you win and encourage others to *cherish* their progress. Believe you can *conquer* any obstacle. Don't be afraid to *confront* difficult issues. *Likewise*, have something to *contribute* to what's happening. *Finally, be confident, competent*, and *competitive*.

如何成功

　　要獲得成功，首先你必須追求你的夢想。當你贏的時候要歡呼，並鼓勵別人珍惜他們的進步。要相信你能克服任何的阻礙。不要害怕面對困難的問題。同樣地，對發生的事要有貢獻。最後，要有信心、要能幹，並且競爭心要強。

IV. 填空：

　　Success won't come on its own.　You must ___1___ your dreams until they come true.　___2___ others when they achieve success.　And of course, ___3___ your time and use it wisely.

　　What's more, have faith in yourself to ___4___ your fears and ___5___ all of life's difficulties.　It's important to ___6___ your best effort.

　　Above all, a ___7___ person gains respect.　A ___8___ person is capable and much in demand.　A ___9___ person loves a challenge.

　　成功不會自己來。你必須追求你的夢想，直到它們實現。當別人成功時，要為他們喝采。當然，要珍惜你的時間，並聰明地使用。

　　此外，要對自己有信心，相信自己能克服恐懼，並面對人生中所有的困難。貢獻你最大的努力是很重要的。

　　最重要的是，有信心的人才能獲得尊重。能幹的人很有能力，並且很搶手。競爭心強的人很喜歡挑戰。

【解答】1. chase　2. Cheer　3. cherish　4. conquer　5. confront
　　　　6. contribute　7. confident　8. competent　9. competitive
　　　　* **on** *one's* **own** 獨自；憑自己　　faith〔feθ〕*n.* 信心
　　　　capable〔ˋkepəbḷ〕*adj.* 有能力的
　　　　much in demand 需求量大　　challenge〔ˋtʃælɪndʒ〕*n.* 挑戰

V. 詞彙題：

Directions: *Choose the one word that best completes the sentence.*

1. _____ after what you want in life, and you will get it.
   (A) Chatter   (B) Chase   (C) Cheat   (D) Choose

2. _____ when others achieve success.
   (A) Choke   (B) Chant   (C) Cheer   (D) Chew

3. _____ each and every day as a gift.
   (A) Cherish   (B) Clarify   (C) Clench   (D) Classify

4. The successful person is able to _____ any fear.
   (A) concentrate   (B) condense   (C) confer   (D) conquer

5. When the time comes, _____ the challenges.
   (A) confuse   (B) confirm   (C) confront   (D) connect

6. Always work hard and _____ your best effort.
   (A) congratulate   (B) contribute   (C) confess   (D) contradict

7. Relax and be _____ in your abilities.
   (A) confident   (B) concrete   (C) continental   (D) contrary

8. Strive to be _____ in whatever you do.
   (A) common   (B) compact   (C) competent   (D) complex

9. Successful people are _____ and live for challenges.
   (A) comparative   (B) complete   (C) commercial
   (D) competitive

【答案】1.（B）　2.（C）　3.（A）　4.（D）　5.（C）　6.（B）
　　　　7.（A）　8.（C）　9.（D）

VI. 同義字整理：

1. **chase** 〔 tʃes 〕 v. 追求
   = pursue 〔 pɚˈsu 〕
   = follow 〔 ˈfɑlo 〕
   = go after

2. **cheer** 〔 tʃɪr 〕 v. 歡呼
   = applaud 〔 əˈplɔd 〕
   = encourage 〔 ɪnˈkɝɪdʒ 〕

3. **cherish** 〔 ˈtʃɛrɪʃ 〕 v. 珍惜
   = treasure 〔 ˈtrɛʒɚ 〕
   = prize 〔 praɪz 〕
   = love 〔 lʌv 〕

4. **conquer** 〔 ˈkɑŋkɚ 〕 v. 征服；克服
   = defeat 〔 dɪˈfit 〕
   = overcome 〔 ˌovɚˈkʌm 〕
   = master 〔 ˈmæstɚ 〕

5. **confront** 〔 kənˈfrʌnt 〕 v. 面對
   = face 〔 fes 〕
   = deal with
   = cope with

6. **contribute** 〔 kənˈtrɪbjut 〕 v. 貢獻
   = give 〔 gɪv 〕
   = supply 〔 səˈplaɪ 〕
   = provide 〔 prəˈvaɪd 〕
   = chip in

7. **confident** 〔 ˈkɑnfədənt 〕 adj. 有信心的
   = self-assured 〔 ˈsɛlf əˈʃurd 〕
   = bold 〔 bold 〕
   = certain 〔 ˈsɝtn̩ 〕

8. **competent** 〔 ˈkɑmpətənt 〕 adj. 能幹的
   = capable 〔 ˈkepəbl̩ 〕
   = able 〔 ˈebl̩ 〕
   = skilled 〔 skɪld 〕

9. **competitive** 〔 kəmˈpɛtətɪv 〕 adj. 好競爭的
   = aggressive 〔 əˈgrɛsɪv 〕
   = ambitious 〔 æmˈbɪʃəs 〕
   = relentless 〔 rɪˈlɛntlɪs 〕

How to Succeed

4. C (2)

看英文唸出中文	一口氣說九句	看中文唸出英文
control² (kən'trol) v. n.	字首是 Con { *Control.* 要掌控。	控制
concentrate⁴ ('kɑnsn̩‚tret) v.	*Concentrate.* 要專心。	專心
cultivate⁶ ('kʌltə‚vet) v.	*Cultivate.* 要培養。	培養

cooperate⁴ (ko'ɑpə‚ret) v.	字首是 Coo { *Cooperate.* 要合作。	字尾是 ate	合作
coordinate⁶ (ko'ɔrdn̩‚et) v.	*Coordinate.* 要協調。	使協調
create² (krɪ'et) v.	*Create.* 要創造。	創造

communicate³ (kə'mjunə‚ket) v.	字首都是 Com { *Communicate.* 要溝通。	溝通
complete² (kəm'plit) v.	*Complete.* 要完成。	完成
commit⁴ (kə'mɪt) v.	*Commit* yourself. 要投入。	使致力於

I. 背景說明：

Control.（要掌控。）可說成：Be in *control*.（要掌控。）
Control the situation.（要控制情況。）(= *Take control of the*
situation.) *Concentrate*.（要專心。）可說成：*Concentrate*
on the task at hand.（要專心於手邊的工作。）*Concentrate* on
what's important.（要專心於重要的事。）*Cultivate*.（要培養。）
可說成：*Cultivate* good relationships.（要培養良好的關係。）
Cultivate your business.（要發展你的事業。）*Cultivate* good
manners.（要培養良好的禮貌。）

Cooperate.（要合作。）可說成：*Cooperate* with others.
（要和別人合作。）Encourage people to *cooperate* with you.
（要鼓勵大家和你一起合作。）*Coordinate*.（要協調。）可說
成：*Coordinate* with your partners.（要和你的夥伴協調。）
Coordinate your priorities.（要協調你的優先事項。）*Create*.
（要創造。）可說成：*Create* your success.（要創造你的成
功。）*Create* good things.（要創造美好的事物。）

Communicate.（要溝通。）可說成：*Communicate*
effectively.（要有效地溝通。）*Communicate* positively.（要
積極地溝通。）(= *Communicate in a positive way*.) *Complete*.
（要完成。）可說成：*Complete* the task.（要完成任務。）
Complete what you start.（要有始有終。）*Commit yourself*.
（要投入。）可說成：*Commit yourself* to success.（要為成功
而全心投入。）*Commit yourself* to a goal.（要為一個目標全心
投入。）

II. 英語演講：

【一字英語演講】　　【短篇英語演講】

Hello, everybody:　　*Hello, everybody:* 大家好：

Control.　　*Control* the situation. 要控制情況。
Concentrate.　　*Concentrate* on the task at hand.
Cultivate.　　要專心於手邊的工作。
　　Cultivate good manners. 要培養良好的禮貌。
Cooperate.
Coordinate.　　Encourage people to *cooperate* with you.
Create.　　要鼓勵大家和你一起合作。
　　Coordinate with your partners.
Communicate.　　要和你的夥伴協調。
Complete.　　*Create* good things. 要創造美好的事物。
Commit yourself.
　　Communicate positively. 要積極地溝通。
Now you know　　*Complete* the task. 要完成任務。
　how to succeed.　　*Commit yourself* to a goal.
　　要為一個目標全心投入。

　　Now you know how to succeed.
　　現在你知道如何才能成功了。

III. 短篇作文：

Create Success

　　Let's look at some of the ways we can succeed that start with the letter "c". *To begin with, control* the situation, *concentrate* on what's important, and *cultivate* good relationships. *Next, commit yourself* to a purpose, *cooperate* with others, and *coordinate* your priorities. *Finally, communicate* effectively and *complete* whatever you start. You've just *created* your own success.

創造成功

　　我們來看看一些開頭字母是 "c"，能讓我們成功的方法。首先，要控制情況、專心於重要的事，並培養良好的關係。其次，要爲一個目標全心投入、和別人合作，並協調你的優先事項。最後，要有效地溝通，並且要有始有終。你已經創造了自己的成功。

> * purpose〔'pɝpəs〕*n.* 目的；目標
> priority〔praɪ'ɔrətɪ〕*n.* 優先的事物

IV. 填空：

　　To succeed, you must ___1___ your own destiny. ___2___ on the important tasks. ___3___ good manners in order to establish relationships.

　　Meanwhile, encourage people to ___4___ with you. ___5___ with your partners. In this way, you can ___6___ good things.

　　Last but not least, ___7___ positively. ___8___ the task at hand before starting something else. ___9___ yourself to the greater goal.

　　要成功，你必須掌控自己的命運。要專注於重要的任務。要培養良好的禮貌，以建立人際關係。

　　同時，要鼓勵大家和你一起合作。要和你的夥伴協調。如此一來，你就可以創造美好的事物。

　　最後一項要點是，要積極地溝通。在開始做別的事之前，要完成手邊的工作。要爲更偉大的目標全心投入。

【解答】1. control　2. Concentrate　3. Cultivate　4. cooperate
　　　　5. Coordinate　6. create　7. communicate
　　　　8. Complete　9. Commit
　　　　* destiny〔'dɛstənɪ〕*n.* 命運　meanwhile〔'min,hwaɪl〕*adv.* 同時
　　　　last but not least 最後一項要點是

V. 詞彙題：

Directions: *Choose the one word that best completes the sentence.*

1. Learn how to _____ your emotions instead of getting upset.
   (A) commemorate   (B) contend   (C) control   (D) contact

2. _____ on the task at hand and don't get distracted.
   (A) Concentrate   (B) Conceive   (C) Concern   (D) Conclude

3. Be diplomatic and _____ good relationships.
   (A) consist   (B) cultivate   (C) console   (D) consume

4. The job is easier when we _____ with each other.
   (A) convince   (B) convict   (C) continue   (D) cooperate

5. Get together with your partner and _____ your plans.
   (A) correspond   (B) contain   (C) coordinate   (D) convey

6. By staying active, you _____ new opportunities to advance.
   (A) create   (B) cram   (C) creep   (D) criticize

7. A successful person knows to _____ with people.
   (A) commute   (B) communicate   (C) comfort   (D) complain

8. _____ everything you start.
   (A) Condemn   (B) Comprise   (C) Comply   (D) Complete

9. Wake up every morning and _____ yourself to success.
   (A) command   (B) commence   (C) commit   (D) combat

【答案】 1. (C)   2. (A)   3. (B)   4. (D)   5. (C)   6. (A)
　　　　 7. (B)   8. (D)   9. (C)

VI. 同義字整理：

1. **control** 〔 kən'trol 〕 *v. n.* 控制
   - = lead 〔 lid 〕
   - = rule 〔 rul 〕
   - = direct 〔 də'rɛkt 〕
   - = command 〔 kə'mænd 〕

2. **concentrate** 〔'kɑnsn̩,tret 〕 *v.* 專心
   - = focus 〔'fokəs 〕
   - = pay attention to
   - = keep *one's* mind on

3. **cultivate** 〔'kʌltə,vet 〕 *v.* 培養
   - = improve 〔 ɪm'pruv 〕
   - = establish 〔 ə'stæblɪʃ 〕
   - = develop 〔 dɪ'vɛləp 〕

4. **cooperate** 〔 ko'ɑpə,ret 〕 *v.* 合作
   - = work together
   - = collaborate 〔 kə'læbə,ret 〕

5. **coordinate** 〔 ko'ɔrdn̩,et 〕 *v.* 使協調
   - = organize 〔'ɔrgən,aɪz 〕
   - = synchronize 〔'sɪŋkrə,naɪz 〕
   - = integrate 〔'ɪntə,gret 〕
   - = mesh 〔 mɛʃ 〕

6. **create** 〔 krɪ'et 〕 *v.* 創造
   - = produce 〔 prə'djus 〕
   - = make 〔 mek 〕
   - = develop 〔 dɪ'vɛləp 〕
   - = form 〔 fɔrm 〕

7. **communicate** 〔 kə'mjunə,ket 〕 *v.* 溝通
   - = contact 〔'kɑntækt 〕
   - = talk 〔 tɔk 〕
   - = correspond 〔,kɔrə'spɑnd 〕
   - = be in touch

8. **complete** 〔 kəm'plit 〕 *v.* 完成
   - = finish 〔'fɪnɪʃ 〕
   - = accomplish 〔 ə'kɑmplɪʃ 〕
   - = fulfill 〔 fʊl'fɪl 〕

9. **commit yourself** 要投入
   - = dedicate yourself
   - = devote yourself

How to Succeed

5. D (1)

看英文唸出中文	一口氣說九句	看中文唸出英文
desire[2] 〔 dɪˋzaɪr 〕 *v. n.*	字首都是 De *Desire.* 要渴望成功。	渴望
demand[4] 〔 dɪˋmænd 〕 *v.*	*Demand.* 要要求。	要求;需要
determine[3] 〔 dɪˋtɝmɪn 〕 *v.*	*Determine.* 要有決心。	決定;決心

devote[4] 〔 dɪˋvot 〕 *v.*	字首是 Dev *Devote.* 要奉獻。	奉獻;使致力於
develop[2] 〔 dɪˋvɛləp 〕 *v.*	*Develop.* 要發展。	發展
discover[1] 〔 dɪˋskʌvɚ 〕 *v.*	字首是 Dis *Discover.* 要發現。	發現

discuss[2] 〔 dɪˋskʌs 〕 *v.*	*Discuss.* 要討論。	討論
defeat[4] 〔 dɪˋfit 〕 *v.*	字首是 De *Defeat* fear. 要戰勝恐懼。	打敗
dedicate[6] 〔 ˋdɛdəˏket 〕 *v.*	*Dedicate* yourself. 要全心投入。	使致力於;奉獻

I. 背景説明：

Desire. （要渴望成功。）(= *Desire to be successful.*)
Visualize what you *desire* and go for it. （想像你所渴望的，
並全力以赴。）desire 也可當名詞。No success without
desire. （不想成功，就不會成功。）*Demand*. （要要求。）
可説成：*Demand* excellence in your work. （工作要要求完
美。）Provide what the situation *demands*. （提供情況所需
要的事物。）*Determine*. （要有決心。）*Determine* to be
successful. （決心要成功。）*Determine* a goal. （要決定一個
目標。）*Determine* your priority. （要決定你的優先順序。）
decide 和 determine 都表示「決定」，但後者語氣較強。成功
的人能夠把握機會，下定決心，做一個很快的決定。

　　Devote. （要奉獻。）可説成：*Devote* yourself. （要全心
投入。）*Devote* all your energy to improvement. （貢獻你所
有的精力去改善。）*Develop*. （要發展。）可説成：*Develop*
your skills. （要發展你的技能。）Seek to *develop* strong
relationships. （要試圖培養穩固的關係。）*Discover*. （要發
現。）可説成：*Discover* your unused potential. （要發現你尚
未使用的潛力。）Seek to *discover* new ways. （要試圖發現新
方法。）

　　Discuss. （要討論。）可説成：*Discuss* your plans with
others. （要和別人討論你的計劃。）Be open and *discuss* your
ideas. （要公開討論你的想法。）*Defeat fear*. （要戰勝恐懼。）
可説成：*Defeat* your enemies. （要打敗你的敵人。）

Defeat your competitors.（要打敗你的競爭對手。）defeat
也可當名詞，作「失敗」解，說成：Don't accept the *defeat*.
（不要接受失敗。）*Defeat* is a learning experience.（失
敗是個學習的經驗。）*Dedicate yourself.*（要全心投入。）可
說成：*Dedicate* your efforts to the goal.（要奉獻你的努力，
達成目標。）*Dedicate* your time.（要付出你的時間。）不捨
得付出時間、上班覺得累、等待下班，都沒辦法成功。不捨
得下班、不想下班、喜歡加班，都是成功者的特性。*Dedicate*
your resources to success.（要對成功付出你的資源。）

【句中的 to 等於 toward】

Boys and girls.

Desire.
Demand.
Determine.

Devote.
Develop.
Discover.

Discuss.
Defeat fear.
Dedicate yourself.

Success is waiting for you.

II. 短篇英語演講：

Boys and girls: 各位男孩，各位女孩：

Desire to be successful. 要渴望成功。
Provide what the situation *demands*.
要提供情況所需要的事物。
Determine a goal. 要決定一個目標。

Devote yourself. 要全心投入。
Develop your skills. 要發展你的技能。
Seek to *discover* new ways. 要試圖發現新方法。

Discuss your plans. 要討論你的計劃。
Defeat your *fear*. 要戰勝你的恐懼。
Dedicate yourself to hard work. 要全心投入努力工作。

Success is waiting for you. 成功正等待著你。

III. 短篇作文：

How to Be a Successful Person

To begin with, visualize what you *desire* and go for it.
Demand excellence in your work. *Determine* to be
successful. *Next*, *devote* all your energy to improvement.
Seek to *develop* strong relationships. *Discover* your inner
potential. Be open, *discuss* your idea, and *defeat* fear.
Finally, *dedicate* your efforts to the goal.

如何成爲一個成功的人

首先，要想像你所渴望的，並全力以赴。工作要要求完美。決心要成功。其次，要貢獻你所有的精力去改善。要試圖培養穩固的關係。要發現你內在的潛力。要公開討論你的想法，並戰勝恐懼。最後，要奉獻你的努力，達成目標。

IV. 填空：

You must ___1___ to be successful. Provide what the situation ___2___. ___3___ a goal and go for it.

Meanwhile, to achieve success, you should ___4___ yourself to hard work. ___5___ your skills. Seek to ___6___ new ways of doing things.

Most importantly, ___7___ your plans with others. ___8___ your competitors. ___9___ your time to an important cause or issue. destiny ('dɛstənɪ) *n.* 命

你必須渴望成功。提供情況所需要的事物。要決定一個目標，並全力以赴。

同時，想要獲得成功，你應該全心投入，努力工作。要發展你的技能。要試圖發現做事情的新方法。

最重要的是，要和別人討論你的計劃。要打敗你的競爭對手。要爲重要的目標或議題付出你的時間。

【解答】 1. desire　2. demands　3. Determine　4. devote
　　　　　5. Develop　6. discover　7. discuss　8. Defeat
　　　　　9. Dedicate

　　*　competitor (kəm'pɛtətə) *n.* 競爭者
　　　 cause (kɔz) *n.* (造福於人的) 事業；活動；目標
　　　 issue ('ɪʃju) *n.* 議題；問題

V. 詞彙題：

Directions: *Choose the one word that best completes the sentence.*

1. A person who _____ to succeed can't be stopped.
   (A) descends　(B) destroys　(C) despises　(D) desires

2. Provide what the situation _____, and you will succeed.
   (A) demands　(B) depends　(C) derives　(D) depicts

3. To achieve anything, first, you must _____ a goal.
   (A) depress　(B) delay　(C) determine　(D) degrade

4. _____ yourself to reaching your goal and think of nothing else.
   (A) Detach　(B) Devote　(C) Detect　(D) Deter

5. Take the time to _____ your skills as well as you can.
   (A) devour　(B) develop　(C) detain　(D) depart

6. Seek to _____ new and improved methods.
   (A) discourage　(B) discard　(C) discover　(D) disconnect

7. Solve problems by _____ the situation calmly with others.
   (A) discussing　(B) disgusting　(C) displacing
   (D) disguising

8. Work hard to _____ the competition.
   (A) deliver　(B) defeat　(C) dictate　(D) dissolve

9. Be _____ to your mission and be willing to sacrifice.
   (A) defended　(B) designed　(C) disposed　(D) dedicated

【答案】 1. (D)　2. (A)　3. (C)　4. (B)　5. (B)　6. (C)
　　　　 7. (A)　8. (B)　9. (D)

VI. 同義字整理：

1. **desire** ﹝ dɪˋzaɪr ﹞ *v. n.* 渴望
   - = want ﹝ wɑnt ﹞
   - = crave ﹝ krev ﹞
   - = wish for
   - = hope for

2. **demand** ﹝ dɪˋmænd ﹞ *v.* 要求；
   需要
   - = request ﹝ rɪˋkwɛst ﹞
   - = ask for
   - = call for

3. **determine** ﹝ dɪˋtɝmɪn ﹞ *v.*
   決定；決心
   - = resolve ﹝ rɪˋzɑlv ﹞
   - = make up *one's* mind

4. **devote** ﹝ dɪˋvot ﹞ *v.* 奉獻；
   使致力於
   - = dedicate ﹝ˋdɛdəˌket ﹞
   - = commit ﹝ kəˋmɪt ﹞

5. **develop** ﹝ dɪˋvɛləp ﹞ *v.* 發展
   - = grow ﹝ gro ﹞
   - = create ﹝ krɪˋet ﹞
   - = increase ﹝ ɪnˋkris ﹞

6. **discover** ﹝ dɪˋskʌvɚ ﹞
   v. 發現
   - = find ﹝ faɪnd ﹞
   - = locate ﹝ˋloket , loˋket ﹞
   - = learn ﹝ lɝn ﹞

7. **discuss** ﹝ dɪˋskʌs ﹞ *v.* 討論
   - = talk about
   - = argue about
   - = exchange ideas

8. **defeat fear** 戰勝恐懼
   - = conquer anxiety
   - = overcome weakness

9. **dedicate yourself**
   要全心投入
   - = commit yourself
   - = devote yourself

How to Succeed

6. D (2)

看英文唸出中文	一口氣說九句	看中文唸出英文
decide[1] 〔 dɪˈsaɪd 〕 v.	字首是 De	***Decide.*** 要做出決定。	決定
devise[4] 〔 dɪˈvaɪz 〕 v.		***Devise.*** 要設計。	設計
dominate[4] 〔ˈdɑməˌnet 〕 v.		***Dominate.*** 要掌控一切。	支配；控制

---

dare[3] 〔 dɛr 〕 v.	字首是 Da	***Dare.*** 要勇敢。	敢；勇敢
dazzle[5] 〔ˈdæzl̩ 〕 v.		***Dazzle.*** 要使人印象深刻。	使目眩
differentiate[6] 〔ˌdɪfəˈrɛnʃɪˌet 〕 v.	都有 Differ	***Differentiate.*** 要懂得區別。	區別

---

differ[4] 〔ˈdɪfɚ 〕 v.	字首都是 Di	***Differ.*** 要與眾不同。	不同
dispose[5] 〔 dɪˈspoz 〕 v.		***Dispose.*** 要會處理。	處置
diversify[6] 〔 dəˈvɝsəˌfaɪ 〕 v.		***Diversify.*** 要多樣化。	使多樣化

I. 背景說明：

Decide.（要做出決定。）可加長為：*Decide* what you want to do.（要決定你想要做什麼。）*Decide* what you want and go for it.（要決定你想要什麼，並全力以赴。）*Devise.*（要設計。）*Devise* a plan.（要設計一個計劃。）*Devise* a method.（要想出一個方法。）devise 可作「設計；發明；想出」解。*Dominate.*（要掌控一切。）(= *Dominate everything.*) *Dominate* your competitor.（要掌控你的競爭對手。）

Dare.（要勇敢。）可說成：*Dare* to be different.（要勇於與眾不同。）*Dazzle.*（要使人印象深刻。）可說成：*Dazzle* the competition.（要使對手驚奇。）【competition〔͵kɑmpə'tɪʃən〕*n.* 競爭者】*Dazzle* the audience.（要使觀眾印象深刻。）(= *Impress the audience.*) dazzle 的意思有「使目眩；使驚奇；使讚嘆不已；使傾倒」。*Differentiate.*（要懂得區別。）*Differentiate* between good and bad.（要懂得區別好與壞。）Learn how to *differentiate.*（要學會如何區別。）

Differ.（要與眾不同。）可說成：It's good sometimes to *differ.*（有時候與眾不同是好事。）Don't be afraid to *differ.*（不要害怕與眾不同。）*Dispose.*（要會處理。）可說成：*Dispose* of what you don't need.（要處理你不需要的東西。）*Dispose* of excess.（要處理多餘的東西。）【excess〔ɪk'sɛs〕*n.* 過多；過量；過度】*Diversify.*（要多樣化。）可說成：*Diversify* your skills.（要學會多種技能。）*Diversify* your range of knowledge.（你的知識範圍要廣泛。）

II. 英語演講：

【一字英語演講】

Friends:

Decide.
Devise.
Dominate.

Dare.
Dazzle.
Differentiate.

Differ.
Dispose.
Diversify.

Get ready to be successful!

【短篇英語演講】

Friends: 朋友們：

Decide what you want to do.
要決定你想要做什麼。
Devise a method. 要想出一個方法。
Dominate your competitor.
要掌控你的競爭對手。

Dare to improve. 要勇於改進。
Dazzle the competition. 要使對手驚奇。
Learn how to *differentiate*. 要學會如何區別。

Don't be afraid to *differ*. 不要害怕與眾不同。
Dispose of what you don't need.
要處理你不需要的東西。
Diversify your range of knowledge.
你的知識範圍要廣泛。

Get ready to be successful! 準備迎接成功吧！

III. 短篇作文：

The Way to Success

　　Here's the way to success. *Decide* what you want and go for it. *Devise* a plan. *Dominate* your competitor. *Dare* to be different. *Dazzle* the audience. It's good sometimes to *differ*. *Differentiate* between good and bad. *Dispose* of excess. *Diversify* your skills. Success is guaranteed.

成功之道

以下就是成功之道。要決定你想要什麼，並全力以赴。要設計一個計劃。要掌控你的競爭對手。要勇於與眾不同。要使觀眾印象深刻。有時候與眾不同是好事。要懂得區別好與壞。要處理多餘的東西。要學會多種技能。你一定會成功。

* guarantee〔͵gærən′ti〕*v.* 保證

IV. 填空：

The first step on the way to success is to ___1___ what you want to do. ___2___ a plan to make it happen. Only then can you ___3___ your competitor.

Therefore, ___4___ to try something different. ___5___ the competition with your fresh idea. Learn how to ___6___ between good and bad.

Above all, don't be afraid to ___7___ if you don't agree with somebody. ___8___ of the things that aren't going to help you succeed. ___9___ your range of knowledge.

邁向成功的第一步，就是決定你想要做什麼。要設計一個計劃，然後趕快去做。唯有如此，你才能掌控你競爭對手。

因此，要勇於嘗試不同的事。要用新奇的想法使對手驚奇。要學會如何區別好與壞。

最重要的是，如果你不同意某人，不要害怕與眾不同。要處理那些不會幫助你成功的事物。你的知識範圍要廣泛。

【解答】 1. decide　2. Devise　3. dominate　4. dare
5. Dazzle　6. differentiate　7. differ　8. Dispose
9. Diversify
* fresh〔frɛʃ〕*adj.* 新的；新鮮的　　range〔rendʒ〕*n.* 範圍

V. 詞彙題：

Directions: *Choose the one word that best completes the sentence.*

1. You cannot proceed until you _____ what you want.
   (A) decline　(B) decide　(C) direct　(D) deceive

2. Do your research before _____ a plan.
   (A) devising　(B) delegating　(C) diagnosing
   (D) deteriorating

3. Be strong and _____ your challengers.
   (A) donate　(B) dodge　(C) dominate　(D) download

4. You must be willing to _____ to try new things.
   (A) decay　(B) distress　(C) disable　(D) dare

5. You will _____ them with your winning smile.
   (A) dazzle　(B) dread　(C) dump　(D) dwell

6. Learn how to _____ between good and evil.
   (A) disturb　(B) define　(C) differentiate　(D) disregard

7. If you _____ with someone, do so politely.
   (A) damage　(B) differ　(C) decrease　(D) defend

8. _____ of the things you don't need.
   (A) Demonstrate　(B) Distinguish　(C) Deposit　(D) Dispose

9. Increase your value by _____ your skills.
   (A) diverting　(B) distorting　(C) diversifying　(D) dismissing

【答案】 1.（B）　2.（A）　3.（C）　4.（D）　5.（A）　6.（C）
　　　　　7.（B）　8.（D）　9.（C）

VI. 同義字整理：

1. **decide** 〔 dɪ'saɪd 〕 v. 決定
   = determine 〔 dɪ'tɝmɪn 〕
   = choose 〔 tʃuz 〕
   = resolve 〔 rɪ'zɑlv 〕
   = make up *one's* mind

2. **devise** 〔 dɪ'vaɪz 〕 v. 設計
   = plan 〔 plæn 〕
   = form 〔 fɔrm 〕
   = imagine 〔 ɪ'mædʒɪn 〕

3. **dominate** 〔'dɑmə,net 〕 v.
   支配；控制
   = control 〔 kən'trol 〕
   = rule 〔 rul 〕
   = lead 〔 lid 〕
   = direct 〔 də'rɛkt 〕

4. **dare** 〔 dɛr 〕 v. 敢；勇敢
   = risk doing
   = venture 〔'vɛntʃɚ 〕
   = have the courage to

5. **dazzle** 〔'dæzḷ 〕 v. 使目眩
   = impress 〔 ɪm'prɛs 〕
   = amaze 〔 ə'mez 〕
   = fascinate 〔'fæsṇ,et 〕

6. **differentiate** 〔,dɪfə'rɛnʃɪ,et 〕 v.
   區別
   = distinguish 〔 dɪ'stɪŋgwɪʃ 〕
   = separate 〔'sɛpə,ret 〕
   = discriminate 〔 dɪ'skrɪmə,net 〕

7. **differ** 〔'dɪfɚ 〕 v. 不同
   = contradict 〔,kɑntrə'dɪkt 〕
   = contrast 〔 kən'træst 〕

8. **dispose** 〔 dɪ'spoz 〕 v. 處置
   = get rid of
   = eliminate 〔 ɪ'lɪmə,net 〕
   = discard 〔 dɪs'kɑrd 〕

9. **diversify** 〔 də'vɝsə,faɪ 〕 v. 使多
   樣化
   = vary 〔'vɛrɪ 〕
   = change 〔 tʃendʒ 〕
   = expand 〔 ɪk'spænd 〕

How to Succeed

7. E

看英文唸出中文	一口氣說九句	看中文唸出英文
express[2] 〔 ɪkˈsprɛs 〕v.	字首是 Exp { *Express*. 要會表達。	表達
explore[4] 〔 ɪkˈsplor 〕v.	*Explore*. 要去探索。	探險；探測
eloquent[6] 〔ˈɛləkwənt 〕adj.	Be *eloquent*. 口才要好。	口才好的

---

encourage[2] 〔 ɪnˈkɝɪdʒ 〕v.	字首是 En { *Encourage*. 要鼓勵。	鼓勵
endeavor[5] 〔 ɪnˈdɛvɚ 〕v.	*Endeavor*. 要努力。	努力
evolve[6] 〔 ɪˈvɑlv 〕v.	*Evolve*. 要發展。	進化；發展

---

excel[5] 〔 ɪkˈsɛl 〕v.	字首都是 ex { *Excel*. 要勝過別人。	勝過他人；突出； 非常擅長
execute[5] 〔ˈɛksɪˌkjut 〕v.	*Execute*. 要執行。	執行
excellent[2] 〔ˈɛksḷənt 〕adj.	Be *excellent*. 要很優秀。	優秀的

EXCELLENT

* excel 是 excellent 的動詞。

I. 背景説明：

Express.（要會表達。）可説成：*Express* yourself clearly.（要清楚地表達你的意思。）*Express* your enthusiasm for the project.（要表達出你對計劃的熱情。）*Explore*.（要去探索。）*Explore* the unknown territory.（要探索未知的領域。）*Explore* the new technology.（要探索新的科技。）*Be eloquent*.（口才要好。）(= *Be an eloquent speaker*.)

Encourage.（要鼓勵。）可説成：*Encourage* others.（要鼓勵別人。）A good leader *encourages* others to try harder.（好的領導者會鼓勵別人更努力。）*Endeavor*.（要努力。）可説成：*Endeavor* to lead.（要努力領導。）*Endeavor* to work hard.（要努力工作。）(= *Try to work hard*.) Be moral in whatever you *endeavor*.（不管你努力做什麼，都要有道德心。）*Evolve*.（要發展。）Allow your thinking to *evolve*.（要擴大你的想法。）(= *Allow your mind to expand*.)

Excel.（要勝過別人。）可説成：*Excel* at what you do.（做什麼事都要做到最好。）It takes hard work to *excel* at anything.（要很努力才能把任何事都做到最好。）*Execute*.（要執行。）可説成：*Execute* your plans.（要執行你的計劃。）*Execute* the orders.（要執行命令。）*Be excellent*.（要很優秀。）可加長為：*Be excellent* in everything you do.（做什麼事都要做到最好。）*Be* an *excellent* leader.（要做一個優秀的領導者。）

II. 英語演講：

【一字英語演講】

Dear friends and associates:

Express.
Explore.
Be eloquent.

Encourage.
Endeavor.
Evolve.

Excel.
Execute.
Be excellent.

Success will come.

【短篇英語演講】

Dear friends and associates:
親愛的朋友和同事們：

Express yourself clearly.
要清楚地表達你的意思。
Explore new technologies. 要探索新的科技。
Be an *eloquent* speaker. 口才要好。

Encourage others. 要鼓勵別人。
Endeavor to lead. 要努力領導。
Allow your thinking to *evolve*. 要擴大你的想法。

Excel at what you do. 做什麼事都要做到最好。
Execute the orders. 要執行命令。
Be an *excellent* leader. 要做一個優秀的領導者。

Success will come. 成功將會來到。

III. 短篇作文：

How to Find Success

Expressing yourself clearly is a sure way to find success. *Be* an *eloquent* speaker. *Explore* the unknown territory and *encourage* others to do the same. *Endeavor* to work hard and be moral in everything you do. It takes hard work to *excel* at anything. *At the same time*, you have to allow your thinking to *evolve*. *But in the end*, if you *execute* your plans, you'll be *excellent* in everything you do.

如何找到成功

清楚地表達你的意思,是個能確保你找到成功的方法。口才要好。要探索未知的領域,並且鼓勵別人也這麼做。要努力工作,並且做任何事都要有道德心。需要很努力,才能把任何事都做到最好。同時,你必須要擴大你的想法。不過到最後,如果你能執行你的計劃,那你做什麼事都能做到最好。

* territory〔ˋtɛrəˌtorɪ〕*n.* 領土;領域

IV. 填空:

____1____ yourself clearly and you'll be on your way to success. ____2____ new technologies. Be an ____3____ speaker.

____4____ others to try harder. Likewise, ____5____ to work hard and be moral in everything you do. However, you have to allow your thinking to ____6____.

In the end, you must ____7____. Work to ____8____ the orders. You will be an ____9____ leader.

如果你能清楚地表達你的意思,你就會邁向成功。要探索新的科技。口才要好。

要鼓勵別人更努力。同樣地,要努力工作,並且無論做什麼,都要有道德心。然而,你必須要擴大你的想法。

最後,你必須要勝過別人。要努力執行命令。你將會是一個優秀的領導者。

【解答】 1. Express 2. Explore 3. eloquent 4. Encourage
5. endeavor 6. evolve 7. excel 8. execute
9. excellent

V. 詞彙題：

Directions: *Choose the one word that best completes the sentence.*

1. Be clear and precise when _____ your feelings.
   (A) exporting　(B) expressing　(C) expiring　(D) extracting

2. Don't hesitate to _____ new methods and technologies.
   (A) excite　(B) exist　(C) expel　(D) explore

3. Be pure in thought and _____ in speech.
   (A) eloquent　(B) evident　(C) electrical　(D) edible

4. _____ others to pursue their dreams and be their best.
   (A) Encounter　(B) Endanger　(C) Encourage　(D) Enclose

5. _____ to acquire as much knowledge as you can.
   (A) Enlighten　(B) Endeavor　(C) Enlarge　(D) Enforce

6. Your methods must _____ in order to stay current.
   (A) evaluate　(B) establish　(C) erupt　(D) evolve

7. It takes years of diligent practice to _____ in anything.
   (A) explode　(B) excel　(C) exchange　(D) expect

8. You'd better _____ your plans as soon as you can.
   (A) exhaust　(B) excuse　(C) execute　(D) exile

9. _____ leaders always listen more than they speak.
   (A) Excellent　(B) Extreme　(C) Extensive　(D) Extinct

【答案】1.（B）　2.（D）　3.（A）　4.（C）　5.（B）　6.（D）
　　　　7.（B）　8.（C）　9.（A）

VI. 同義字整理：

1. **express** 〔 ɪkˈsprɛs 〕 *v.* 表達
   - = state 〔 stet 〕
   - = communicate 〔 kəˈmjunəˌket 〕
   - = say 〔 se 〕

2. **explore** 〔 ɪkˈsplor 〕 *v.* 探險；
   探測
   - = investigate 〔 ɪnˈvɛstəˌget 〕
   - = consider 〔 kənˈsɪdɚ 〕
   - = research 〔 rɪˈsɝtʃ 〕

3. **eloquent** 〔ˈɛləkwənt 〕 *adj.*
   口才好的
   - = articulate 〔 ɑrˈtɪkjəlɪt 〕
   - = well-spoken 〔ˈwɛlˈspokən 〕

4. **encourage** 〔 ɪnˈkɝɪdʒ 〕 *v.* 鼓勵
   - = cheer 〔 tʃɪr 〕
   - = inspire 〔 ɪnˈspaɪr 〕
   - = comfort 〔ˈkʌmfɚt 〕

5. **endeavor** 〔 ɪnˈdɛvɚ 〕 *v.* 努力
   - = undertake 〔ˌʌndɚˈtek 〕
   - = try 〔 traɪ 〕
   - = attempt 〔 əˈtɛmpt 〕
   - = make an effort

6. **evolve** 〔 ɪˈvɑlv 〕 *v.* 進化；
   發展
   - = grow 〔 gro 〕
   - = develop 〔 dɪˈvɛləp 〕
   - = advance 〔 ədˈvæns 〕

7. **excel** 〔 ɪkˈsɛl 〕 *v.* 勝過他人；
   突出；非常擅長
   - = exceed 〔 ɪkˈsid 〕
   - = surpass 〔 sɚˈpæs 〕
   - = outdo 〔ˌaʊtˈdu 〕
   - = go beyond

8. **execute** 〔ˈɛksɪˌkjut 〕 *v.* 執行
   - = enforce 〔 ɪnˈfors 〕
   - = implement 〔ˈɪmpləˌmɛnt 〕
   - = carry out

9. **excellent** 〔ˈɛkslənt 〕 *adj.*
   優秀的
   - = outstanding 〔ˈaʊtˈstændɪŋ 〕
   - = brilliant 〔ˈbrɪljənt 〕
   - = great 〔 gret 〕

How to Succeed

8. *F*

看英文唸出中文	一 口 氣 說 九 句	看中文唸出英文
follow[1] (ˈfɑlo) v. **focus**[2] (ˈfokəs) v. **found**[3] (faʊnd) v.	字首都是 Fo *Follow*. 要遵守。 *Focus*. 要專注。 *Found*. 要建立。	跟隨;遵守 集中 建立
forgive[2] (fəˈgɪv) v. **fortify**[6] (ˈfɔrtə,faɪ) v. **forecast**[4] (ˈfor,kæst) v.	字首都是 For *Forgive*. 要原諒。 *Fortify*. 要強化。 *Forecast*. 要預測。	原諒 強化 預測
face[1] (fes) v. **firm**[2] (fɜm) adj. **flexible**[4] (ˈflɛksəbl̩) adj.	字首都是 f *Face*. 要勇於面對。 Be *firm*. 要堅定。 Be *flexible*. 要有彈性。	面對 堅定的 有彈性的;可變通的;靈活的

I. 背景説明：

Follow.（要遵守。）可説成：*Follow* the rules.（要遵守規定。）*Follow* the program.（要跟著計劃走。）【program〔'progræm〕 *n.* 計劃】*Focus*.（要專注。）可説成：*Focus* on what you want to achieve.（要專心做你想要達成的事。）Train yourself to *focus* on the goal.（要訓練自己鎖定目標。）*Found*.（要建立。）*Found* your own company.（要建立自己的公司。）*Found* your own business.（要建立自己的事業。）

Forgive.（要原諒。）可説成：*Forgive* those who have wronged you.（要原諒那些誤解你的人。）*Forgive* people for little mistakes.（要原諒犯小錯的人。）*Fortify*.（要強化。）可説成：*Fortify* yourself.（要強化自己。）*Fortify* your team.（要強化你的團隊。）*Forecast*.（要預測。）可説成：*Forecast* success.（要預測成功。）*Forecast* the future.（要預測未來。）

Face.（要勇於面對。）可説成：*Face* the challenge.（要勇於面對挑戰。）*Face* the difficulty.（要勇於面對困難。）*Be firm*.（要堅定。）可説成：*Be firm* and resolute.（要非常堅定。）【resolute〔'rɛzə,lut〕 *adj.* 堅決的】Have a *firm* handshake.（要用力握手。）*Be flexible*.（要有彈性。）可説成：*Be flexible* with time.（時間要有彈性。）有必要時，可以更改計劃。（= *Change your plans when necessary.*）*Be a flexible* person.（要做個懂得變通的人。）

II. 英語演講：

【一字英語演講】　【短篇英語演講】

My dear friends:　*My dear friends:* 親愛的朋友：

Follow.　*Follow* the rules. 要遵守規定。
Focus.　*Focus* on what you want to achieve.
Found.　要專心做你想要達成的事。
　Found your own business.
Forgive.　要建立自己的事業。
Fortify.
Forecast.　*Forgive* those who have wronged you.
　要原諒那些誤解你的人。
Face.　*Fortify* yourself. 要強化自己。
Be firm.　*Forecast* the future. 要預測未來。
Be flexible.
　Face the challenge. 要勇於面對挑戰。
These are keys to　*Be firm* and resolute. 要非常堅定。
　success.　*Be* a *flexible* person. 要做個懂得變通的人。

　These are keys to success. 這些就是成功的關鍵。

III. 短篇作文：

The Keys to Success

　　Success is guaranteed to those who *follow* a program. *Indeed*, you must train yourself to *focus* on your goals. *Found* your own business. *At the same time*, *forgive* mistakes and *fortify* your team. *Forecast* the future. *Face* the difficulties of life. *Also*, have a *firm* handshake. *Finally*, *be flexible* with time.

成功的關鍵

凡是遵照計劃的人，一定會成功。的確，你必須訓練自己，專注於你的目標。要建立自己的事業。同時，要原諒錯誤，並強化你的團隊。要預測未來。要勇於面對人生的困難。此外，要用力握手。最後，時間要有彈性。

IV. 填空：

By ____1____ a simple routine, success can be yours. ____2____ on a goal and ____3____ your own company.

To begin with, ____4____ those who have wronged you. ____5____ yourself with lots of exercise and good nutrition. ____6____ positive things to happen in the future.

Finally, ____7____ every challenge.　Be a ____8____ but fair leader.　However, be ____9____ with your time.

藉由遵循簡單的程序，成功就可能是你的。要鎖定目標，並創立自己的公司。

首先，要原諒那些誤解你的人。要做許多運動，並攝取良好的營養來強化自己。要預測未來會有好事發生。

最後，要勇於面對每個挑戰。要做個堅定但公平的領導者。不過，你的時間要有彈性。

【解答】 1. following　2. Focus　3. found　4. forgive
　　　　 5. Fortify　6. Forecast　7. face　8. firm
　　　　 9. flexible
　　　　 * routine〔ruˋtin〕n. 例行公事；程序
　　　　　 wrong〔rɔŋ〕v. 誤解；冤枉

V. 詞彙題：

Directions: *Choose the one word that best completes the sentence.*

1. Successful people make a plan and ＿＿＿＿＿＿ the schedule.
   (A) flourish　(B) forsake　(C) forbid　(D) follow

2. ＿＿＿＿＿＿ completely on what you want to achieve.
   (A) Flock　(B) Focus　(C) Flash　(D) Flatter

3. The successful person is driven to ＿＿＿＿＿＿ his own company.
   (A) found　(B) fold　(C) flutter　(D) float

4. It's better to ＿＿＿＿＿＿ and forget when people harm you.
   (A) flunk　(B) form　(C) forgive　(D) filter

5. Eat right and get a lot of exercise to ＿＿＿＿＿＿ yourself.
   (A) fortify　(B) fascinate　(C) facilitate　(D) foresee

6. Use your intuition to ＿＿＿＿＿＿ the future.
   (A) falter　(B) fling　(C) furnish　(D) forecast

7. When the time comes, ＿＿＿＿＿＿ the challenge before you.
   (A) fade　(B) face　(C) flap　(D) fulfill

8. Make a decision and stand ＿＿＿＿＿＿ with your choice.
   (A) fake　(B) fierce　(C) firm　(D) fertile

9. ＿＿＿＿＿＿ people are willing to accommodate last minute changes.
   (A) Favorable　(B) Flexible　(C) Fatal　(D) Federal

【答案】1. (D)　2. (B)　3. (A)　4. (C)　5. (A)　6. (D)
　　　　7. (B)　8. (C)　9. (B)

VI. 同義字整理：

1. **follow**〔'falo〕*v.* 跟隨；遵守
   - = obey〔ə'be〕
   - = observe〔əb'zɝv〕
   - = comply with

2. **focus**〔'fokəs〕*v.* 集中
   - = concentrate〔'kɑnsn̩,tret〕
   - = pinpoint〔'pɪn,pɔɪnt〕
   - = zero in on

3. **found**〔faʊnd〕*v.* 建立
   - = establish〔ə'stæblɪʃ〕
   - = form〔fɔrm〕
   - = start〔stɑrt〕

4. **forgive**〔fɚ'gɪv〕*v.* 原諒
   - = excuse〔ɪk'skjuz〕
   - = pardon〔'pɑrdn̩〕

5. **fortify**〔'fɔrtə,faɪ〕*v.* 強化
   - = strengthen〔'strɛŋθən〕
   - = reinforce〔,riɪn'fors〕
   - = support〔sə'port〕

6. **forecast**〔'for,kæst〕*v.* 預測
   - = predict〔prɪ'dɪkt〕
   - = anticipate〔æn'tɪsə,pet〕
   - = foresee〔for'si〕

7. **face**〔fes〕*v.* 面對
   - = confront〔kən'frʌnt〕
   - = meet〔mit〕
   - = encounter〔ɪn'kaʊntɚ〕

8. **firm**〔fɝm〕*adj.* 堅定的
   - = steady〔'stɛdɪ〕
   - = solid〔'sɑlɪd〕
   - = stable〔'stebl̩〕

9. **flexible**〔'flɛksəbl̩〕*adj.* 有彈性的；可變通的；靈活的
   - = adaptable〔ə'dæptəbl̩〕
   - = variable〔'vɛrɪəbl̩〕
   - = open〔'opən〕

 **How to Succeed**

9. G

看英文唸出中文	一 口 氣 說 九 句	看中文唸出英文
grow[1] 〔 gro 〕 *v.*	字首是 Gro	*Grow.* 要成長。	成長
grope[6] 〔 grop 〕 *v.*		*Grope.* 要摸索。	摸索；尋找
glow[3] 〔 glo 〕 *v.*		*Glow.* 要發光。	發光

(表格分隔線)

grab[3] 〔 græb 〕 *v.*	字首是同義字 Gra	*Grab.* 要抓住機會。	抓住
grasp[3] 〔 græsp 〕 *v.*		*Grasp.* 要抓住挑戰。	抓住
guide[1] 〔 gaɪd 〕 *v.*		*Guide.* 要引導別人。	引導

(表格分隔線)

generate[6] 〔ˈdʒɛnəˌret 〕 *v.*	字首是 gener	*Generate.* 要有生產力。	產生
generous[2] 〔ˈdʒɛnərəs 〕 *adj.*		Be *generous.* 要慷慨。	慷慨的
grateful[4] 〔ˈgretfəl 〕 *adj.*		Be *grateful.* 要心存感激。	感激的

I. 背景説明：

  Grow.（要成長。）可説成：Use every opportunity to *grow.*（要利用每一個機會成長。）*Grow* from your experience.（要從你的經驗中成長。）*Grope.*（要摸索。）grope 的意思有「摸索；探索；尋找」。可説成：*Grope* for success.（要尋求成功。）(= *Go get success.*) *Grope* for achievement.（要尋求成就。）*Glow.*（要發光。）可加強語氣説成：*Glow* with enthusiasm for your work.（要發出對工作有熱忱的光芒。）You should *glow* brightly.（你應該閃閃發光。）

  Grab.（要抓住。）可説成：*Grab* every chance you get.（抓住你所得到的每一次機會。）Don't hesitate to *grab* an opportunity.（不要猶豫去抓住機會。）*Grasp.*（要抓住。）(= *Grab.*) *Grasp* opportunity.（要抓住機會。）*Grasp* any challenge.（要抓住任何挑戰的機會。）Grab. 常用，一般語氣，Grasp. 少用，語氣較強。*Guide.*（要引導。）可説成：*Guide* others through difficulty.（要引導別人度過難關。）*Guide* others to success.（要帶領別人邁向成功。）

  Generate.（要有生產力。）generate 的主要意思是「產生」(= *produce*)，還可作「創造」解 (= *create*)。你要成功，就必須產生收入 (generate income)、產生出熱情 (generate passion)、產生熱忱 (generate enthusiasm)。這句話可説成：*Generate* interest in your work.（要對工作產生興趣。）

Be generous.（要慷慨。）可說成：Be *generous* with your time.（要願意付出你的時間。）Be *generous* with your money.（用錢要慷慨。）*Be grateful*.（要心存感激。）可說成：Be *grateful* when others help you.（當別人幫助你時，要心存感激。）Have a *grateful* attitude.（要有心存感激的態度。）

　　用「英文一字金」可編成短篇和長篇演講。

II. 短篇英語演講：

Greetings, everyone! 大家好！

Grow from your experience. 要從你的經驗中成長。
Grope for achievement. 要尋求成就。
Glow with enthusiasm for your work.
要發出對工作有熱忱的光芒。

Grab every chance you get. 抓住你所得到的每一次機會。
Grasp any challenge. 要抓住任何挑戰的機會。
Guide others through difficulty. 要引導別人度過難關。

Generate interest in your work. 要對工作產生興趣。
Be generous with your money. 用錢要慷慨。
Be grateful when others help you.
當別人幫助你時，要心存感激。

Success will be yours! 你會成功的！

III. 短篇作文：

The Secret of Success

In order to succeed, you must use every opportunity to *grow*. You have to *grope* for achievement. You should *glow* with enthusiasm for what you're doing. *Therefore*, *grab* and *grasp* any challenge. *Guide* others through difficulty. *Besides*, *generate* interest in your business. *Be generous* with your money and have a *grateful* attitude. That's the secret of success.

成功的祕訣

爲了要成功，你必須利用每一個機會成長。你必須尋求成就。你應該要發出對你所做的事有熱忱的光芒。因此，要抓住任何挑戰的機會。要引導別人度過難關。此外，要對你的事業產生興趣。用錢要慷慨，而且要有心存感激的態度。這就是成功的祕訣。

IV. 填空：

If you are looking for success, try to ___1___ from every experience. ___2___ for achievement. ___3___ with enthusiasm for your work.

Likewise, ___4___ every opportunity that comes your way. ___5___ any challenge. A successful person knows how to ___6___ others through difficulty.

Finally, ___7___ interest in your work. Be ___8___ with your money. Be ___9___ when others help you.

如果你正在尋求成功，試著從每一次的經驗中成長。要尋求成就。要發出對工作有熱忱的光芒。

同樣地，要抓住每一個你碰到的機會。要抓住任何挑戰的機會。成功的人知道如何引導別人度過難關。

最後，要對你的工作產生興趣。用錢要慷慨。當別人幫助你時，要心存感激。

【解答】 1. grow　2. Grope　3. Glow　4. grab　5. Grasp
6. guide　7. generate　8. generous　9. grateful
* enthusiasm〔ɪnˈθjuzɪˌæzəm〕*n.* 熱忱
come** one's **way 發生在某人身上；被某人碰到

V. 詞彙題：

Directions: *Choose the one word that best completes the sentence.*

1. Use every experience as a chance to _____ as an individual.
   (A) grow   (B) gain   (C) gaze   (D) gasp

2. Constantly _____ for success.
   (A) grant   (B) graze   (C) grieve   (D) grope

3. _____ with enthusiasm for your work.
   (A) Glare   (B) Glance   (C) Glow   (D) Glide

4. The wise man _____ every opportunity that comes his way.
   (A) guesses   (B) grabs   (C) growls   (D) grins

5. _____ all, lose all.
   (A) Grasp   (B) Govern   (C) Greet   (D) Gnaw

6. _____ others through tough times.
   (A) Glitter   (B) Giggle   (C) Guide   (D) Gossip

7. You must _____ interest in your work.
   (A) generalize   (B) gamble   (C) graduate   (D) generate

8. Be _____ with your money and with your time.
   (A) generous   (B) genetic   (C) global   (D) grand

9. Be _____ when others help you.
   (A) graphic   (B) grateful   (C) gloomy   (D) grim

【答案】 1.（A） 2.（D） 3.（C） 4.（B） 5.（A） 6.（C）
　　　　 7.（D） 8.（A） 9.（B）

VI. 同義字整理：

1. **grow** 〔 gro 〕 *v.* 成長

> = increase 〔 ɪn'kris 〕
> = improve 〔 ɪm'pruv 〕
> = develop 〔 dɪ'vɛləp 〕

2. **grope** 〔 grop 〕 *v.* 摸索；尋找

> = search 〔 sɝtʃ 〕
> = reach for

3. **glow** 〔 glo 〕 *v.* 發光

> = shine 〔 ʃaɪn 〕
> = gleam 〔 glim 〕

4. **grab** 〔 græb 〕 *v.* 抓住

> = seize 〔 siz 〕
> = grasp 〔 græsp 〕
> = take hold

5. **grasp** 〔 græsp 〕 *v.* 抓住

> = grip 〔 grɪp 〕
> = hold 〔 hold 〕
> = catch 〔 kætʃ 〕

6. **guide** 〔 gaɪd 〕 *v.* 引導

> = lead 〔 lid 〕
> = direct 〔 də'rɛkt 〕
> = show the way

7. **generate** 〔'dʒɛnə,ret 〕 *v.* 產生

> = create 〔 krɪ'et 〕
> = produce 〔 prə'djus 〕
> = make 〔 mek 〕

8. **generous** 〔'dʒɛnərəs 〕 *adj.* 慷慨的

> = hospitable 〔'hɑspɪtəbl̩ 〕
> = charitable 〔'tʃærətəbl̩ 〕
> = unselfish 〔 ʌn'sɛlfɪʃ 〕

9. **grateful** 〔'gretfəl 〕 *adj.* 感激的

> = thankful 〔'θæŋkfəl 〕
> = appreciative 〔 ə'priʃɪ,etɪv 〕
> = obliged 〔 ə'blaɪdʒd 〕

How to Succeed

10. H

看英文唸出中文	一口氣說九句	看中文唸出英文
helpful[2] 〔ˈhɛlpfəl〕 *adj.*	Be *helpful*. 要樂於助人。	樂於助人的
hopeful[4] 〔ˈhopfəl〕 *adj.*	*Hopeful*. 要充滿希望。	充滿希望的
humorous[3] 〔ˈhjumərəs〕 *adj.*	*Humorous*. 要幽默。	幽默的

字首都是 h　字尾是 ful
* helpful 接上一課的 grateful。

---

humble[2] 〔ˈhʌmbḷ〕 *adj.*	*Humble*. 要謙虛。	謙虛的
honorable[4] 〔ˈɑnərəbḷ〕 *adj.*	*Honorable*. 要讓人尊敬。	光榮的;可敬的
hospitable[6] 〔ˈhɑspɪtəbḷ〕 *adj.*	*Hospitable*. 要好客。	好客的

字首是 Ho　字尾都是 ble

---

hardy[5] 〔ˈhardɪ〕 *adj.*	*Hardy*. 身體要強健。	強健的
hearty[5] 〔ˈhartɪ〕 *adj.*	*Hearty*. 要真心誠意。	真誠的
healthy[2] 〔ˈhɛlθɪ〕 *adj.*	*Healthy*. 要保持健康。	健康的

字首是 Hea　字尾都是 y

I. 背景説明：

Be helpful.（要樂於助人。）可加強語氣説成：Always *be helpful*.（永遠都要樂於助人。）尤其是在別人困難的時候，你要第一個跳出來，去幫助別人。Find ways to *be helpful*.（要找到方法去幫助別人。）*Hopeful*.（要充滿希望。）(= *Be hopeful*.) 可説成：Remain *hopeful*.（要一直充滿希望。）*Humorous*.（要幽默。）(= *Be humorous*.) 可説成：*Humorous* people are popular.（幽默的人很受歡迎。）

Humble.（要謙虛。）(= *Be humble*.) 可説成：Be *humble* when you win.（當你贏的時候要謙虛。）*Honorable*.（要讓人尊敬。）(= *Be honorable*. = *Be respectable*.) Do the *honorable* thing.（要做光榮的事。）honorable 的意思有「光榮的；可敬的；值得尊敬的；高尚的；尊貴的」，要看前後句意來翻譯。*Hospitable*.（要好客。）(= *Be hospitable*.) Be a *hospitable* person.（要做一個好客的人。）Have a *hospitable* attitude.（要有好客的態度。）

Hardy.（身體要強健。）(= *Be hardy*.) Be a *hardy* worker.（要做一個強壯又健康的工作者。）Be *hardy* and strong.（要能吃苦耐勞。）*Hearty*.（要真心誠意。）(= *Be hearty*.) Have a *hearty* laugh.（要真誠地笑。）Give *hearty* cooperation.（要真誠地合作。）hearty 的意思是「真誠的；真摯的」(= *friendly and enthusiastic*「友善又熱心」)。*Healthy*.（要保持健康。）(= *Be healthy*. = *Stay healthy*.) Have a *healthy* attitude.（要有健康的心態。）

II. 英語演講：

【一字英語演講】

Dear teachers and students:

Be helpful.
Hopeful.
Humorous.

Humble.
Honorable.
Hospitable.

Hardy.
Hearty.
Healthy.

You will definitely succeed!

【短篇英語演講】

Dear teachers and students: 親愛的老師和同學：

Always *be helpful*. 永遠都要樂於助人。
Remain *hopeful*. 要一直充滿希望。
Humorous people are popular.
幽默的人很受歡迎。

Be *humble* when you win. 當你贏的時候要謙虛。
Do the *honorable* thing. 要做光榮的事。
Have a *hospitable* attitude. 要有好客的態度。

Be a *hardy* worker.
要做一個強壯又健康的工作者。
Have a *hearty* laugh. 要真誠地笑。
Stay *healthy*. 要保持健康。

You will definitely succeed! 你一定會成功！

III. 短篇作文：

Be a Successful Person

Everybody wants to be a successful person. But how do we get there? *First*, you must *be helpful*, *hopeful*, and *humorous*. *Humorous* people are popular. *Second*, be *humble*, *honorable*, and *hospitable*. Do the *honorable* thing. *Third*, be *hardy*, *hearty*, and *healthy*. Be a *hardy* worker. Give *hearty* cooperation. Have a *healthy* attitude. Your success is guaranteed.

做一個成功的人

每個人都想做一個成功的人。但是我們如何才能成功？首先，你必須樂於助人、充滿希望，並且幽默。幽默的人很受歡迎。第二，要謙虛、要讓人尊敬，而且要好客。要做光榮的事。第三，要強健、眞誠，而且健康。要做一個強壯又健康的工作者。要眞誠地合作。要有健康的心態。你一定會成功。

IV. 填空：

Finding ways to be ___1___ is a key to success. By remaining ___2___, you always look on the bright side. At the same time, it's important to be ___3___. People who are funny are popular.

On the other hand, be ___4___ when you win. Always do the ___5___ thing and have a ___6___ attitude.

Also, be a ___7___ and tireless worker. A ___8___ handshake will impress others. But above all, maintaining a ___9___ lifestyle is the number one key to success.

找到方法去幫助別人，是成功的關鍵。一直充滿希望，你就會總是看到事物的光明面。同時，幽默是很重要的。好笑的人很受歡迎。

另一方面，當你贏的時候要謙虛。一定要做光榮的事，而且要有好客的態度。

此外，要做一個強健而且孜孜不倦的工作者。眞誠的握手能使別人印象深刻。但最重要的是，維持健康的生活方式是成功的首要祕訣。

【解答】 1. helpful　2. hopeful　3. humorous　4. humble
　　　　　5. honorable　6. hospitable　7. hardy　8. hearty
　　　　　9. healthy
　　　　　* handshake〔'hænd,ʃek〕*n.* 握手

V. 詞彙題：

Directions: *Choose the one word that best completes the sentence.*

1. Share _____ information with others.
   (A) hoarse   (B) humid   (C) hasty   (D) helpful

2. No matter what happens, remain _____.
   (A) hateful   (B) harmful   (C) hopeful   (D) handful

3. A _____ story will lighten a tense mood.
   (A) humorous   (B) horizontal   (C) hostile   (D) hollow

4. Be _____ when you win and gracious when you lose.
   (A) huge   (B) humble   (C) handicapped   (D) holy

5. Always choose the most _____ path.
   (A) historical   (B) household   (C) honorable   (D) hourly

6. Greet everyone with a _____ attitude.
   (A) hospitable   (B) homesick   (C) heavy   (D) harsh

7. Be a _____ character who can withstand anything.
   (A) handy   (B) hardy   (C) habitual   (D) hi-fi

8. People love to hear a _____ laugh.
   (A) haunted   (B) historic   (C) horrible   (D) hearty

9. Eat right, get plenty of exercise, and stay _____.
   (A) honorary   (B) hysterical   (C) healthy   (D) heavenly

【答案】 1.（D） 2.（C） 3.（A） 4.（B） 5.（C） 6.（A）
   7.（B） 8.（D） 9.（C）

VI. 同義字整理：

1. **helpful**〔ˈhɛlpfəl〕*adj.* 樂於助人的
   - = useful〔ˈjusfəl〕
   - = productive〔prəˈdʌktɪv〕
   - = supportive〔səˈpɔrtɪv〕

2. **hopeful**〔ˈhopfəl〕*adj.* 充滿希望的
   - = optimistic〔ˌɑptəˈmɪstɪk〕
   - = confident〔ˈkɑnfədənt〕
   - = assured〔əˈʃurd〕

3. **humorous**〔ˈhjumərəs〕*adj.* 幽默的
   - = funny〔ˈfʌnɪ〕
   - = amusing〔əˈmjuzɪŋ〕

4. **humble**〔ˈhʌmbḷ〕*adj.* 謙虛的
   - = modest〔ˈmɑdɪst〕
   - = unassuming〔ˌʌnəˈsjumɪŋ〕

5. **honorable**〔ˈɑnərəbḷ〕*adj.* 光榮的；可敬的
   - = admirable〔ˈædmərəbḷ〕
   - = respectable〔rɪˈspɛktəbḷ〕
   - = honest〔ˈɑnɪst〕

6. **hospitable**〔ˈhɑspɪtəbḷ〕*adj.* 好客的
   - = welcoming〔ˈwɛlkəmɪŋ〕
   - = kind〔kaɪnd〕
   - = generous〔ˈdʒɛnərəs〕
   - = friendly〔ˈfrɛndlɪ〕
   - = liberal〔ˈlɪbərəl〕

7. **hardy**〔ˈhɑrdɪ〕*adj.* 強健的
   - = robust〔roˈbʌst〕
   - = vigorous〔ˈvɪgərəs〕
   - = strong〔strɔŋ〕
   - = tough〔tʌf〕

8. **hearty**〔ˈhɑrtɪ〕*adj.* 眞誠的
   - = warm〔wɔrm〕
   - = welcoming〔ˈwɛlkəmɪŋ〕
   - = genuine〔ˈdʒɛnjuɪn〕

9. **healthy**〔ˈhɛlθɪ〕*adj.* 健康的
   - = hardy〔ˈhɑrdɪ〕
   - = blooming〔ˈblumɪŋ〕
   - = robust〔roˈbʌst〕
   - = vigorous〔ˈvɪgərəs〕

How to Succeed

11. I (1)

看英文唸出中文	一口氣說九句	看中文唸出英文
improve² 〔ɪmˋpruv〕v.	字首都是 Imp { *Improve.* 要改善。 *Impress.* 要讓人佩服。 *Implement.* 要執行。	改善
impress³ 〔ɪmˋprɛs〕v.		使印象深刻
implement⁶ 〔ˋɪmpləˏmɛnt〕v.		實施；執行

invent² 〔ɪnˋvɛnt〕v.	字首都是 In { *Invent.* 要發明新東西。 *Initiate.* 要率先開始。 *Innovate.* 要創新。 字尾是 ate	發明
initiate⁵ 〔ɪˋnɪʃɪˏet〕v.		創始；發起
innovate⁶ 〔ˋɪnəˏvet〕v.		創新

＊這三個字意思相近。

invest⁴ 〔ɪnˋvɛst〕v.	字首都是 In { *Invest.* 要投資。 *Inspire.* 要激勵。 *Instruct.* 要教導。 字首是 Ins	投資
inspire⁴ 〔ɪnˋspaɪr〕v.		激勵
instruct⁴ 〔ɪnˋstrʌkt〕v.		教導

I. 背景説明：

Improve.（要改善。）可説成：*Improve* yourself.（要改善自己。）Seek to *improve* your skills.（要試圖改善你的技能。）*Impress*.（要讓人佩服。）Dress to *impress*.（衣服要穿得讓人印象深刻。）*Impress* others.（要讓人忘不了你。）impress 的主要意思是「令人印象深刻」，可引申出很多意思，如「令人難忘」、「讓人佩服」等，要視上下文而定。*Implement*.（要執行。）*Implement* your ideas.（要執行你的想法。）*Implement* the plan.（要執行計劃。）(=*Execute the plan*.)

Invent.（要發明新東西。）(=*Invent new things*.) *Invent* new ways of doing things.（要發明做事的新方法。）*Initiate*.（要率先開始。）可説成：*Initiate* contact.（要先開始和人接觸；要主動先和人接觸。）*Initiate* projects.（要第一個提出計劃。）(=*Start plans*.) *Innovate*.（要創新。）可説成：Try to *innovate*.（要努力創新。）You have to *innovate*.（你必須創新。）

Invest.（要投資。）*Invest* in yourself.（要投資你自己。）*Invest* in your work.（要投資你的工作。）(=*Put effort into your work*.) 努力工作是一項投資。有機會，要投資他人。(*Invest in others*.) *Inspire*.（要激勵。）可説成：*Inspire* others.（要激勵別人。）Be *inspired* to succeed.（要受到別人的激勵邁向成功。）Look for ways to be *inspired*.（要尋找能激勵自己的方法。）*Instruct*.（要教導。）可説成：*Instruct* people.（要教導大家。）*Instruct* your team.（要教導你的團隊。）*Instruct* your employees.（要教導你的員工。）

II. 英語演講：

【一字英語演講】	【短篇英語演講】
Friends, I have important news:	*Friends, I have important news:* 朋友們，我有重要的消息：
Improve. *Impress.* *Implement.*	Seek to *improve* your skills. 要試圖改善你的技能。 Dress to *impress.* 衣服要穿得讓人印象深刻。 *Implement* your ideas. 要執行你的想法。
Invent. *Initiate.* *Innovate.*	*Invent* new things. 要發明新東西。 *Initiate* contact. 要主動先和人接觸。 Try to *innovate.* 要努力創新。
Invest. *Inspire.* *Instruct.*	*Invest* in yourself. 要投資你自己。 Be *inspired* to succeed. 要受到別人激勵邁向成功。 *Instruct* others. 要教導別人。
Get ready for success!	*Get ready for success!* 要準備迎接成功！

III. 短篇作文：

Nine Words for Success

Nine words will help you succeed. They are *improve, impress, implement, invent, initiate, innovate, invest, inspire,* and *instruct.* Every word starts with the letter "i".

First, improve yourself. *Impress* others. *Second, invent* new things. *Initiate* projects. Try to *innovate. Besides, invest* in yourself. *Inspire* yourself and others. *Instruct* people. I'm sure you will achieve success.

九個字讓你成功

有九個字能幫助你成功。它們是改善、使人印象深刻、執行、發明、率先開始、創新、投資、激勵，以及教導。每個字的開頭字母都是 "i"。

首先，要改善自己。要讓人忘不了你。第二，要發明新東西。要第一個提出計劃。要努力創新。此外，要投資你自己。要激勵自己和別人。要教導大家。我相信你一定會成功。

IV. 填空：

Seek to ___1___ your skills so that you can ___2___ people. Don't be afraid to ___3___ a new plan.

For sure, to ___4___ something new, you must have courage to take a risk. A successful person is willing to ___5___ new projects. He will try to ___6___.

Most of all, ___7___ in yourself and in others. By ___8___ others to work hard, and ___9___ them in the proper way of doing things, you're certain to succeed.

要試圖改善你的技能，如此才能使人印象深刻。不要害怕執行新的計劃。

當然，為了發明新東西，你必須要有勇氣冒險。成功的人會願意第一個提出新的計劃。他會努力創新。

最重要的是，要投資你自己和別人。藉由激勵別人努力工作，並教導他們用正確的方式做事，你一定會成功。

【解答】 1. improve　2. impress　3. implement　4. invent
5. initiate　6. innovate　7. invest　8. inspiring
9. instructing

* seek〔sik〕*v.* 試圖　　***for sure*** 當然
proper〔ˈprɑpɚ〕*adj.* 適當的；正確的

V. 詞彙題：

Directions: *Choose the one word that best completes the sentence.*

1. Advance your career by _____ your skills.
   (A) ignoring　(B) improving　(C) implying　(D) imitating

2. People will be _____ by your desire to achieve.
   (A) illustrated　(B) impressed　(C) identified　(D) imported

3. Plan wisely and carefully before _____ your ideas.
   (A) imagining　(B) indulging　(C) implementing
   (D) injuring

4. Use your imagination to _____ something new.
   (A) inherit　(B) insult　(C) invade　(D) invent

5. Expand your network by _____ contact with new people.
   (A) initiating　(B) isolating　(C) irritating　(D) inhabiting

6. Solve a problem by _____ a new method.
   (A) intruding　(B) interfering　(C) innovating　(D) insuring

7. Find worthwhile projects to _____ your time in.
   (A) install　(B) insist　(C) inquire　(D) invest

8. _____ other people to succeed.
   (A) Infer　(B) Inspire　(C) Intend　(D) Interpret

9. Be patient and _____ others good-naturedly.
   (A) instruct　(B) interrupt　(C) intervene　(D) intimidate

【答案】 1.(B)　2.(B)　3.(C)　4.(D)　5.(A)　6.(C)
　　　　7.(D)　8.(B)　9.(A)

VI. 同義字整理：

1. **improve** 〔 ɪmˋpruv 〕 v. 改善
   - = enhance 〔 ɪnˋhæns 〕
   - = refine 〔 rɪˋfaɪn 〕
   - = polish 〔ˋpɑlɪʃ 〕
   - = strengthen 〔ˋstrɛŋθən 〕

2. **impress** 〔 ɪmˋprɛs 〕 v. 使印象深刻
   - = dazzle 〔ˋdæzl 〕
   - = inspire 〔 ɪnˋspaɪr 〕
   - = affect 〔 əˋfɛkt 〕

3. **implement** 〔ˋɪmplə͵mɛnt 〕 v. 實施；執行
   - = execute 〔ˋɛksɪ͵kjut 〕
   - = perform 〔 pɚˋfɔrm 〕
   - = apply 〔 əˋplaɪ 〕

4. **invent** 〔 ɪnˋvɛnt 〕 v. 發明
   - = develop 〔 dɪˋvɛləp 〕
   - = generate 〔ˋdʒɛnə͵ret 〕
   - = devise 〔 dɪˋvaɪz 〕

5. **initiate** 〔 ɪˋnɪʃɪ͵et 〕 v. 創始；發起
   - = start 〔 stɑrt 〕
   - = begin 〔 bɪˋgɪn 〕
   - = launch 〔 lɔntʃ 〕

6. **innovate** 〔ˋɪnə͵vet 〕 v. 創新
   - = begin (something new)
   - = introduce (something new)

7. **invest** 〔 ɪnˋvɛst 〕 v. 投資
   - = devote 〔 dɪˋvot 〕
   - = venture 〔ˋvɛntʃɚ 〕
   - = put in

8. **inspire** 〔 ɪnˋspaɪr 〕 v. 激勵
   - = motivate 〔ˋmotə͵vet 〕
   - = move 〔 muv 〕
   - = cause 〔 kɔz 〕
   - = stimulate 〔ˋstɪmjə͵let 〕

9. **instruct** 〔 ɪnˋstrʌkt 〕 v. 教導
   - = guide 〔 gaɪd 〕
   - = lead 〔 lid 〕
   - = teach 〔 titʃ 〕

How to Succeed

12. I (2)

看英文唸出中文	一 口 氣 說 九 句	看中文唸出英文

insight[6]
(ˈɪnˌsaɪt) *n.*

information[4]
(ˌɪnfɚˈmeʃən) *n.*

imagination[3]
(ɪˌmædʒəˈneʃən) *n.*

字首是 in

Have *insight*.
要有洞察力。

Information.
要有資訊。

Imagination.
要有想像力。

字尾是 ation

洞察力；深入的了解

資訊

想像力

---

integrity[6]
(ɪnˈtɛɡrətɪ) *n.*

ingenuity[6]
(ˌɪndʒəˈnuətɪ) *n.*

intelligence[4]
(ɪnˈtɛlədʒəns) *n.*

字首都是 In

Integrity.
要正直。

Ingenuity.
要聰明。

Intelligence.
要聰明。

字尾是 ity

是同義字

正直；誠實

聰明

智力；聰明才智

---

invaluable[6]
(ɪnˈvæljəbḷ) *adj.*

indispensable[5]
(ˌɪndɪsˈpɛnsəbḷ) *adj.*

impressive[3]
(ɪmˈprɛsɪv) *adj.*

字首是 in

Be *invaluable*.
要很珍貴。

Indispensable.
要不可缺少。

Impressive.
要令人印象深刻。

字尾是 able

珍貴的；無價的

不可或缺的

令人印象深刻的

I. 背景説明：

Have insight.（要有洞察力。）可説成：Be a person of *insight*.（要做一個有洞察力的人。）Use your *insight* to improve.（要用你的洞察力來改善。）*Information*.（要有資訊。）(= *Have information*.）可説成：Seek important *information*.（要尋找重要的資訊。）Value *information*.（要重視資訊。）*Imagination*.（要有想像力。）(= *Have imagination*.）Use your *imagination*.（要利用你的想像力。）

Integrity.（要正直。）(= *Have integrity*.）可加長為：Have *integrity* in everything you do.（無論做什麼事都要正直。）Act with *integrity*.（行爲要正直。）integrity（正直）和 honesty（誠實）有點區別。integrity 是指個性，honesty 表示不説謊。*Ingenuity*.（要聰明。）(= *Have ingenuity*.）Use your *ingenuity*.（要運用你的聰明才智。）Put your *ingenuity* to work.（要運用你的聰明才智。）*Intelligence*.（要聰明。）(= *Have intelligence*.）Develop your *intelligence*.（要變得更聰明。）Use *intelligence* to advance your career.（要用你的聰明才智使你的事業進步。）

Be invaluable.（要很珍貴。）可説成：Be an *invaluable* asset to the company.（要成爲公司無價的資產。）Be an *invaluable* worker.（要做一個珍貴的工作者。）*Indispensable*.（要不可缺少。）(= *Be an indispensable person*.）Be an *indispensable* part of the business.（要成爲企業中不可缺少的一部份。）*Impressive*.（要令人印象深刻。）(= *Be impressive*. = *Be an impressive person*.）Have an *impressive* attitude.（要有令人佩服的態度。）

Ⅱ. 英語演講：

【一字英語演講】

My dearest friends:

Have insight.
Information.
Imagination.

Integrity.
Ingenuity.
Intelligence.

Be invaluable.
Indispensable.
Impressive.

Success is guaranteed.

【短篇英語演講】

My dearest friends: 我最親愛的朋友們：

Be a person of *insight*. 要做一個有洞察力的人。
Seek important *information*. 要尋找重要的資訊。
Use your *imagination*. 要利用你的想像力。

Have *integrity* in everything you do.
無論做什麼事都要正直。
Use your *ingenuity*. 要運用你的聰明才智。
Use *intelligence* to advance your career.
要用你的聰明才智使你的事業進步。

Be an *invaluable* asset to the company.
要成為公司無價的資產。
Be an *indispensable* part of the business.
要成為企業中不可缺少的一部份。
Be an *impressive* person. 要令人印象深刻。

Success is guaranteed. 這樣保證會成功。

Ⅲ. 短篇作文：

How to Succeed in Life

You want to succeed in life, right? Start by using your *insight* to establish what needs to be done. Seek important *information*. Having an active *imagination* will help develop your *intelligence*. *Furthermore*, act with *integrity*. Put your *ingenuity* to work. *Be* an *indispensable* person and an *invaluable* worker. Have an *impressive* attitude. Then you will achieve success.

如何擁有成功的人生

你想要成功，對吧？一開始就要運用你的洞察力，確定需要做什麼。要尋找重要的資訊。有活躍的想像力，將會幫助你變得更聰明。此外，行為要正直。要運用你的聰明才智。要成為不可缺少的人，以及珍貴的工作者。要有令人佩服的態度。那樣你就會成功。

* establish〔ə'stæblɪʃ〕v. 確定；查明　　***put…to work*** 運用

IV. 填空：

People of ___1___ know how to solve problems. They understand the value of ___2___. To achieve success, use your ___3___.

Meanwhile, have ___4___ in everything you do. Use your ___5___ to your advantage. Use ___6___ to advance your career.

Indeed, you'll be an ___7___ asset to the company. Make yourself an ___8___ part of the business. Then you'll be an ___9___ person.

有洞察力的人知道如何解決問題。他們了解資訊的價值。想要成功，就要利用你的想像力。

同時，無論做什麼事都要正直。要利用你的聰明才智。要用你的聰明才智使你的事業進步。

的確，你會成為公司無價的資產。要讓自己成為企業中不可缺少的一部份。那麼你就會成為一個令人印象深刻的人。

【解答】 1. insight　2. information　3. imagination　4. integrity
　　　　 5. ingenuity　6. intelligence　7. invaluable
　　　　 8. indispensable　9. impressive
　　　　 * ***to one's advantage*** 對某人有利

V. 詞彙題：

Directions: *Choose the one word that best completes the sentence.*

1. Talking about your feelings provides _____.
   (A) incense   (B) instinct   (C) injury   (D) insight

2. Remember that _____ is the power to make things happen.
   (A) indignation   (B) inflation   (C) information   (D) infection

3. Use your _____ to solve problems.
   (A) intonation   (B) imagination   (C) intersection
   (D) isolation

4. Always act with honesty and _____.
   (A) inquiry   (B) identity   (C) industry   (D) integrity

5. Most troublesome problems can be solved with _____.
   (A) ignorance   (B) ingenuity   (C) impulse   (D) institution

6. The most important feature of a person is his or her _____.
   (A) intelligence   (B) ingredient   (C) interval
   (D) indifference

7. A person with experience is an _____ asset.
   (A) invaluable   (B) intimate   (C) inevitable   (D) instant

8. A person with knowledge is _____ to any project.
   (A) identical   (B) imaginary   (C) indispensable   (D) intact

9. Be smart and be _____.
   (A) immense   (B) impressive   (C) irritable   (D) inferior

【答案】1.(D)　2.(C)　3.(B)　4.(D)　5.(B)　6.(A)
　　　　7.(A)　8.(C)　9.(B)

VI. 同義字整理：

1. **insight** 〔ˈɪnˌsaɪt 〕 *n.* 洞察力；
   深入的了解
   - = understanding
     〔ˌʌndəˈstændɪŋ 〕
   - = intelligence 〔 ɪnˈtɛlədʒəns 〕
   - = perception 〔 pɚˈsɛpʃən 〕

2. **information** 〔ˌɪnfɚˈmeʃən 〕 *n.*
   資訊
   - = facts 〔 fækts 〕
   - = data 〔ˈdetə 〕
   - = knowledge 〔ˈnɑlɪdʒ 〕

3. **imagination** 〔 ɪˌmædʒəˈneʃən 〕
   n. 想像力
   - = ingenuity 〔ˌɪndʒəˈnjuətɪ 〕
   - = insight 〔ˈɪnˌsaɪt 〕
   - = inspiration 〔ˌɪnspəˈreʃən 〕
   - = wit 〔 wɪt 〕
   - = originality 〔 əˌrɪdʒəˈnælətɪ 〕

4. **integrity** 〔 ɪnˈtɛgrətɪ 〕 *n.*
   正直；誠實
   - = honesty 〔ˈɑnɪstɪ 〕
   - = honor 〔ˈɑnɚ 〕
   - = morality 〔 məˈrælətɪ 〕

5. **ingenuity** 〔ˌɪndʒəˈnuətɪ 〕 *n.*
   聰明；獨創性
   - = cleverness 〔ˈklɛvɚnɪs 〕
   - = genius 〔ˈdʒinjəs 〕
   - = originality 〔 əˌrɪdʒəˈnælətɪ 〕

6. **intelligence** 〔 ɪnˈtɛlədʒəns 〕
   n. 智力；聰明才智
   - = judgement 〔ˈdʒʌdʒmənt 〕
   - = insight 〔ˈɪnˌsaɪt 〕
   - = perception 〔 pɚˈsɛpʃən 〕

7. **invaluable** 〔 ɪnˈvæljəbḷ 〕 *adj.*
   珍貴的；無價的
   - = valuable 〔ˈvæljuəbḷ 〕
   - = priceless 〔ˈpraɪslɪs 〕
   - = precious 〔ˈprɛʃəs 〕

8. **indispensable** 〔ˌɪndɪsˈpɛnsəbḷ 〕
   adj. 不可或缺的
   - = vital 〔ˈvaɪtḷ 〕
   - = essential 〔 ɪˈsɛnʃəl 〕
   - = necessary 〔ˈnɛsəˌsɛrɪ 〕

9. **impressive** 〔 ɪmˈprɛsɪv 〕 *adj.*
   令人印象深刻的
   - = outstanding 〔ˈaʊtˈstændɪŋ 〕
   - = striking 〔ˈstraɪkɪŋ 〕
   - = marvelous 〔ˈmɑrvḷəs 〕

How to Succeed

13. J , K , L

看英文唸出中文	一口氣說九句	看中文唸出英文

join¹
〔 dʒɔɪn 〕 *v.*

Join.
要參與。

參加

judge²
〔 dʒʌdʒ 〕 *v.*

Judge.
要會判斷。

判斷

just¹
〔 dʒʌst 〕 *adj.*

Be *just.*
要公正。

公正的

字首都是 j

字首是 ju

---

keen⁴
〔 kin 〕 *adj.*

Be *keen.*
要渴望成功。

敏銳的;渴望的

keep¹
〔 kip 〕 *v.*

Keep learning.
要持續學習。

持續

knowledge²
〔 'nɑlɪdʒ 〕 *n.*

Have *knowledge.*
要有知識。

知識

字首都是 k

字首是 kee

---

lead¹,⁴
〔 lid 〕 *v.*

Lead.
要領導別人。

帶領

listen¹
〔 'lɪsn̩ 〕 *v.*

Listen.
要傾聽。

聽

loyal⁴
〔 'lɔɪəl 〕 *adj.*

Be *loyal.*
要忠誠。

忠誠的

字首都是 l

I. 背景説明：

Join. (要參與。) 可説成：Join the group. (要參加團體。) Join the discussion. (要參與討論。) Judge. (要會判斷。) 可加長爲：Judge wisely. (要明智地判斷。) judge 也可以當名詞，作「法官；評審」解。Be a good judge of character. (要善於判斷個性。) 【be a good judge of 善於判斷】Be just. (要公正。)(= Be fair.) Be just in your words. (說話要公正。) Be just in your actions. (你的所做所爲要公正。)

Be keen. (要渴望成功。)(= Be keen to succeed.) Have a keen sense of judgement. (要有敏銳的判斷感。) Keep learning. (要持續學習。) 可加長爲：Keep learning new skills. (要持續學習新的技能。) Keep learning new things. (要持續學習新的事物。) Have knowledge. (要有知識。) 可説成：Seek knowledge. (要尋求知識。) Be thirsty for knowledge. (要渴望獲得知識。)

Lead. (要領導別人。) 可説成：Lead by example. (要以身作則。) Lead the team. (要領導團隊。) Listen. (要傾聽。) 可説成：Listen carefully. (要小心地聽。) Listen more, speak less. (要多聽少說。) Be loyal. (要忠誠。)(= Be a loyal person.) 可説成：Be loyal to your company. (要對你的公司忠誠。) Be loyal to your friends. (要對你的朋友忠誠。)

II. 英語演講：

【一字英語演講】	【短篇英語演講】
Friends:	*Friends:* 朋友們：
Join.	*Join* the group. 要參加團體。
Judge.	*Judge* wisely. 要明智地判斷。
Be just.	*Be just* in your words. 說話要公正。
Be keen.	*Be keen* to succeed. 要渴望成功。
Keep learning.	*Keep learning.* 要持續學習。
Have knowledge.	*Have knowledge.* 要有知識。
Lead.	*Lead* by example. 要以身作則。
Listen.	*Listen* carefully. 要小心地聽。
Be loyal.	*Be loyal* to your company. 要對你的公司忠誠。
These are nine keys to success.	*These are nine keys to success.* 這些是九個成功的關鍵。

III. 短篇作文：

Success Can Be Yours

Do you want to be successful? *Join* the discussion. *Judge* wisely. *Be* fair and *just.* Have a *keen* sense of judgement. *Keep learning* new skills. Be thirsty for *knowledge.* *Additionally*, you must *lead* the team by *listening* more and speaking less. It's not easy, but a *loyal* person can do it with ease.

成功會是你的

你想要成功嗎？要參與討論。要明智地判斷。要公平而且公正。要有敏銳的判斷感。要持續學習新的技能。要渴望獲得知識。此外，你必須以多聽少說的方式來領導團隊。這並不容易，但是忠誠的人就能輕易做到。

IV. 填空：

Success comes through participation, so you must ___1___ groups and discussions. Good leaders ___2___ wisely. Successful people are fair and ___3___.

At the same time, develop a ___4___ sense of judgement. You also need to ___5___ learning new skills. Be hungry for ___6___ and experience.

Above all, successful people ___7___ by example. They ___8___ to advice from others and are always ___9___ to their friends, family, and company.

成功來自參與，所以你必須參加團體，並參與討論。好的領導者會明智地判斷。成功的人是公平而且公正的。

同時，要培養敏銳的判斷感。你也必須持續學習新的技能。要渴望獲得知識與經驗。

最重要的是，成功的人會以身作則。他們會聽從別人的勸告，並且總是對朋友、家人，以及公司忠誠。

【解答】　1. join　2. judge　3. just　4. keen　5. keep
　　　　　6. knowledge　7. lead　8. listen　9. loyal
　　　* ***be hungry for*** 渴望

V. 詞彙題：

Directions: *Choose the one word that best completes the sentence.*

1. Get involved and _____ the group.
   (A) jaywalk   (B) jump   (C) join   (D) jog

2. Use your past experience to _____ wisely.
   (A) judge   (B) jingle   (C) jeer   (D) jar

3. Be a righteous and _____ person.
   (A) jealous   (B) just   (C) junior   (D) juicy

4. Be _____ to succeed and share your wealth.
   (A) key   (B) knee   (C) kneel   (D) keen

5. Success is assured, so _____ doing what you're doing.
   (A) knit   (B) knock   (C) keep   (D) kindle

6. With _____, any problem can be overcome.
   (A) knowledge   (B) knuckle   (C) kilogram   (D) ketchup

7. _____ others by being a good example.
   (A) Leap   (B) Lean   (C) Leak   (D) Lead

8. A successful leader _____ carefully to his peers.
   (A) lengthens   (B) listens   (C) launches   (D) liberates

9. Be _____ to your company and friends.
   (A) legal   (B) local   (C) loyal   (D) lousy

【答案】 1.（C） 2.（A） 3.（B） 4.（D） 5.（C） 6.（A）
　　　　 7.（D） 8.（B） 9.（C）

VI. 同義字整理：

1. **join** 〔 dʒɔɪn 〕 *v.* 參加
   - = enter 〔'ɛntɚ 〕
   - = enroll in
   - = sign up for

2. **judge** 〔 dʒʌdʒ 〕 *v.* 判斷
   - = evaluate 〔 ɪ'væljəˌet 〕
   - = rate 〔 ret 〕
   - = consider 〔 kən'sɪdɚ 〕

3. **just** 〔 dʒʌst 〕 *adj.* 公正的
   - = fair 〔 fɛr 〕
   - = righteous 〔'raɪtʃəs 〕
   - = honorable 〔'ɑnərəbḷ 〕

4. **keen** 〔 kin 〕 *adj.* 敏銳的；
   渴望的
   - = eager 〔'igɚ 〕
   - = devoted 〔 dɪ'votɪd 〕
   - = enthusiastic 〔 ɪnˌθjuzɪ'æstɪk 〕

5. **keep learning** 要持續學習
   - = keep growing
   - = keep improving
   - = keep advancing

6. **knowledge** 〔'nɑlɪdʒ 〕 *n.* 知識
   - = understanding
     〔ˌʌndɚ'stændɪŋ 〕
   - = intelligence 〔 ɪn'tɛlədʒəns 〕
   - = judgment 〔'dʒʌdʒmənt 〕

7. **lead** 〔 lid 〕 *v.* 帶領
   - = guide 〔 gaɪd 〕
   - = conduct 〔 kən'dʌkt 〕
   - = control 〔 kən'trol 〕

8. **listen** 〔'lɪsṇ 〕 *v.* 聽
   - = hear 〔 hɪr 〕
   - = observe 〔 əb'zɝv 〕
   - = pay attention

9. **loyal** 〔'lɔɪəl 〕 *adj.* 忠誠的
   - = faithful 〔'feθfəl 〕
   - = true 〔 tru 〕
   - = devoted 〔 dɪ'votɪd 〕

How to Succeed

14. M

看英文唸出中文	一 口 氣 説 九 句	看中文唸出英文
measure [2,4] 〔ˈmɛʒɚ〕 v.	*Measure*. 要衡量衡量。	測量
manage [3] 〔ˈmænɪdʒ〕 v.	字首是 Ma { *Manage*. 要管理。	管理
maintain [2] 〔menˈten〕 v.	*Maintain*. 要維持。	維持
move [1] 〔muv〕 v.	*Move*. 要採取行動。	移動;採取行動
motivate [4] 〔ˈmotəˌvet〕 v.	字首都是 mo { *Motivate*. 要激勵。	激勵
moral [3] 〔ˈmɔrəl〕 adj.	Be *moral*. 要有道德心。	道德的
modify [5] 〔ˈmadəˌfaɪ〕 v.	*Modify*. 要修正。	修正
modest [4] 〔ˈmadɪst〕 adj.	字首是 mod { Be *modest*. 要謙虛。	謙虛的;樸素的
mutual [4] 〔ˈmjutʃʊəl〕 adj.	Encourage *mutual* efforts. 要鼓勵共同努力。	互相的;共同的

I. 背景説明：

Measure.（要衡量衡量。）（= *Consider*.）也就是做什麼事，都要考慮一下。可説成：*Measure* your words.（要斟酌你所説的話。）表示説話前要先想一想。（*Think before you speak*.）*Measure* your progress.（要衡量你的進度。）要注意你正在做的事。（*Pay attention to what you're doing*.）*Manage*.（要管理。）可説成：*Manage* your time wisely.（要聰明地管理你的時間。）*Manage* others well.（要好好管理別人。）*Maintain*.（要維持。）可説成：*Maintain* good relationships.（要維持良好的關係。）*Maintain* personal hygiene.（要維持個人的衛生。）

Move.（要採取行動。）（= *Get moving*.）Plan; then *move*.（先做計劃；然後行動。）*Move* quickly.（要趕快行動。）*Motivate*.（要激勵。）可説成：*Motivate* yourself.（要激勵自己。）*Motivate* others.（要激勵別人。）*Be moral*.（要有道德心。）可説成：*Be moral* and hardworking.（要有道德心，並且努力工作。）*Be moral* and responsible.（要既有道德又負責。）

Modify.（要修正。）可説成：*Modify* your outlook.（要修正你的看法。）Be willing to *modify* your plans.（要願意修正你的計劃。）*Be modest*.（要謙虛。）可説成：*Be modest* and sincere.（要謙虛又真誠。）*Be modest* in dress.（穿衣服要樸素。）*Encourage mutual efforts*.（要鼓勵共同努力。）可説成：Share *mutual* interests.（要利益共享。）Develop *mutual* projects.（要發展共同的計劃。）mutual 的意思是「互相的；共同的」，例如：

A: Great to see you.（很高興見到你。）
B: The feeling is *mutual*.（我也這麼覺得。）

II. 英語演講:

【一字英語演講】 | **【短篇英語演講】**

Hello, friends: | *Hello, friends:* 哈囉，朋友們：

Measure. | *Measure* your words. 要斟酌你說的話。
Manage. | *Manage* your time wisely.
Maintain. | 要聰明地管理你的時間。
 | *Maintain* good relationships. 要維持良好的關係。
Move.
Motivate. | Get *moving.* 要採取行動。
Be moral. | *Motivate* yourself. 要激勵自己。
 | *Be* a *moral* person. 要做個有道德心的人。
Modify.
Be modest. | Be willing to *modify* your plans.
Encourage | 要願意修正你的計劃。
 mutual efforts. | *Be modest* and sincere. 要謙虛又真誠。
 | *Encourage mutual efforts.* 要鼓勵共同努力。
Follow these
 keys to success. | *Follow these keys to success.*
 | 要遵循這些成功的關鍵。

III. 短篇作文:

Guidance for Success

Success can be yours by following a few guidelines. *First, measure* your words, *manage* your time wisely, and *maintain* good relationships. *Next, move* quickly, *motivate* others, and *be moral* and hardworking. *Finally, modify* your outlook, *be* a *modest* person, and *encourage mutual efforts.* Say hello to success!

成功的指導方針

　　藉由遵循一些指導方針，成功就可能是你的。首先，要斟酌你說的話，聰明地管理你的時間，並且維持良好的關係。其次，要趕快行動、激勵別人，而且要有道德心，並努力工作。最後，要修正你的看法、做個謙虛的人，並且要鼓勵共同努力。向成功打個招呼吧！

IV. 填空：

　　Thinking before you speak is a good example of ___1___ your words. ___2___ your time wisely is a key to ___3___ good relationships.

　　Most important of all, get ___4___ on your latest project. Do whatever is necessary to ___5___ yourself. Additionally, be a ___6___ and responsible leader.

　　However, you must be willing to ___7___ your schedule if necessary. Be ___8___ and sincere. Encourage ___9___ efforts to achieve success.

　　說話前先想一想，是個斟酌你所說的話的好例子。聰明地管理你的時間，是維持良好關係的關鍵。

　　最重要的是，要開始進行你最新的計劃。做需要做的任何事，來激勵你自己。此外，要做個有道德心又負責任的領導者。

　　然而，如果有必要，你必須願意修正你的時間表。要謙虛又真誠。要鼓勵共同努力，以獲得成功。

【解答】 1. measuring　2. Managing　3. maintaining
　　　　　4. moving　5. motivate　6. moral　7. modify
　　　　　8. modest　9. mutual

V. 詞彙題：

Directions: *Choose the one word that best completes the sentence.*

1. To avoid mistakes, _____ your words before speaking.
   (A) mediate   (B) measure   (C) merge   (D) migrate

2. _____ your time efficiently in order to avoid wasting it.
   (A) Marvel   (B) Manufacture   (C) Manifest   (D) Manage

3. It takes work to _____ good relationships.
   (A) maintain   (B) memorize   (C) mislead   (D) murmur

4. Success isn't stationary, so get _____.
   (A) mourning   (B) moaning   (C) moving   (D) mopping

5. Find ways to _____ yourself every day.
   (A) motivate   (B) mimic   (C) mingle   (D) minimize

6. Be aware of your _____ obligation to be honest.
   (A) medical   (B) militant   (C) mild   (D) moral

7. Sometimes it's necessary to _____ your plans.
   (A) major   (B) march   (C) mash   (D) modify

8. Be _____ about your past successes.
   (A) marine   (B) magnetic   (C) modest   (D) majestic

9. Seek _____ success with your peers.
   (A) manual   (B) mutual   (C) mature   (D) medieval

【答案】 1.(B)　 2.(D)　 3.(A)　 4.(C)　 5.(A)　 6.(D)
　　　　 7.(D)　 8.(C)　 9.(B)

VI. 同義字整理：

1. **measure**〔ˈmɛʒɚ〕*v.* 測量；
   衡量
   = plan〔plæn〕
   = consider〔kənˈsɪdɚ〕
   = calculate〔ˈkælkjə‚let〕

2. **manage**〔ˈmænɪdʒ〕*v.* 管理
   = run〔rʌn〕
   = handle〔ˈhændḷ〕
   = command〔kəˈmænd〕

3. **maintain**〔menˈten〕*v.* 維持
   = sustain〔səˈsten〕
   = retain〔rɪˈten〕
   = keep up

4. **move**〔muv〕*v.* 移動；採取
   行動
   = act〔ækt〕
   = take action
   = take the initiative

5. **motivate**〔ˈmotə‚vet〕*v.* 激勵
   = inspire〔ɪnˈspaɪr〕
   = stimulate〔ˈstɪmjə‚let〕
   = cause〔kɔz〕

6. **moral**〔ˈmɔrəl〕*adj.* 道德的
   = just〔dʒʌst〕
   = ethical〔ˈɛθɪkḷ〕
   = decent〔ˈdisṇt〕

7. **modify**〔ˈmɑdə‚faɪ〕*v.* 修正
   = alter〔ˈɔltɚ〕
   = change〔tʃendʒ〕
   = adapt〔əˈdæpt〕

8. **modest**〔ˈmɑdɪst〕*adj.* 謙虛
   的；樸素的
   = humble〔ˈhʌmbḷ〕
   = moderate〔ˈmɑdərɪt〕
   = unassuming〔‚ʌnəˈsjumɪŋ〕

9. **encourage mutual efforts**
   要鼓勵共同努力
   = promote common
     benefits

How to Succeed

15. M , N

看英文唸出中文	一口氣說九句	看中文唸出英文
master[1] 〔'mæstɚ 〕v.	*Master.* 要精通你的專業技術。	精通
mobilize[6] 〔'mobḷ,aɪz 〕v.	字首是Mo { *Mobilize.* 要會動員。	動員
modernize[5] 〔'mɑdɚn,aɪz 〕v.	*Modernize.* 要跟上時代。 } 字尾是ize	使現代化

---

nourish[6] 〔'nɝɪʃ 〕v.	*Nourish.* 要會培養。	滋養
nurture[6] 〔'nɝtʃɚ 〕v.	字首都是N { *Nurture.* 要會培育。	養育
negotiate[4] 〔 nɪ'goʃɪ,et 〕v.	*Negotiate.* 要會協商。	談判；協商

---

neat[2] 〔 nit 〕adj.	Be *neat.* 要整潔。	整潔的
normal[3] 〔'nɔrmḷ 〕adj.	字首是No { *Normal.* 要正常。	正常的
noticeable[5] 〔'notɪsəbḷ 〕adj.	*Noticeable.* 要引人注目。	顯著的； 明顯的

*要注意 noticeable 的重音。

I. 背景説明：

    Master*.*（要精通你的專業技術。）(= *Master your skills.*）
Master your emotions.（要控制你的情緒。）master 的意思是
「精通；控制」。***Mobilize****.*（要會動員。）可説成：***Mobilize***
others to work hard.（要會動員他人努力工作。）***Mobilize***
your talents.（要會運用你的才能。）mobilize 有「動員」和
「運用」的意思。要成功，就要學會動員，能動員越多人，表
示能力越強。***Modernize****.*（要跟上時代。）可説成：***Modernize***
your thinking.（你的想法要跟上時代。）***Modernize*** your
business skills.（你的商業技巧要跟得上時代。）business
skills 是「商業技巧」(= *ability or knowledge of business
methods such as advertisng or proposals*)。商業技巧要跟得上
時代，如以前廣告是靠報紙、電視，現在是網路、手機。

    Nourish*.*（要會培養。）可説成：***Nourish*** your talents.
（要培養你的才能。）你有天才或才能都需要培養。***Nourish***
the talents of others.（要培養他人的才能。）***Nurture****.*（要
會培育。）***Nurture*** others.（要培育別人。）***Nurture*** your
passion.（要培養你的愛好。）nourish 和 nurture 意思很接
近，但不完全相同，我們也可以説 ***Nourish*** your passion.
【正】，但不能説 *Nourish others.*（誤）要區別這兩個字太麻煩
了，花費了功夫和時間划不來，背短句是最簡單的方法。像
在字典上，nourish 的意思有「滋養；培育；培養」，nurture
「養育；培育」。英文一字多義，要看上下文來判斷它的意思。

Negotiate.（要會協商。）可説成：*Negotiate* a better deal.（要協商出一個較好的交易。）*Negotiate* the contracts.（合約要協商。）

　　Be neat.（要整潔。）（= *Be a neat person.*）Have a *neat* appearance.（外表要整潔。）*Normal*.（要正常。）（= *Be a normal person.*）Act like a *normal* person.（舉止要像一個中規中矩的人。）*Noticeable*.（要引人注目。）（= *Be noticeable.*）動詞是 notice〔ˋnotɪs〕v. 注意到，所以重音在前面，不能唸成 noˊticeable（誤）。Make your enthusiasm *noticeable*.（你的熱忱要讓大家看到。）

要隨時隨地用「英文一字金」演講，可以激勵別人和自己，又練習了英文，一舉三得！

Dear students:

Master.
Mobilize.
Modernize.

Nourish.
Nurture.
Negotiate.

Be neat.
Normal.
Noticeable.

You will be successful.

II. 短篇英語演講：

Dear students: 親愛的同學：

Master your skills. 要精通你的專業技術。
Mobilize others to work hard. 要會動員他人努力工作。
Modernize your thinking. 你的想法要跟上時代。

Nourish your talents. 要培養你的才能。
Nurture your passion. 要培養你的愛好。
Negotiate a better deal. 要協商出一個較好的交易。

Be neat in appearance. 外表要整潔。
Act like a *normal* person. 舉止要像一個中規中矩的人。
Make your enthusiasm *noticeable*.
你的熱忱要讓大家看到。

You will be successful. 你會成功的。

III. 短篇作文：

If You Want to Succeed

If you want to succeed, you must *master* your skills. *Mobilize* others to work hard. *Modernize* your business skills while *nourishing* and *nurturing* the talents of others. A successful person knows how to *negotiate*. *Above all*, *be neat* in appearance, *normal* in behavior, and *noticeable* in your desire to succeed.

如果你想要成功

　　如果你想要成功，就必須精通你的專業技術。要會動員他人努力工作。你的商業技巧要跟得上時代，同時也要培養他人的才能。成功的人知道如何協商。最重要的是，外表要整潔、行為要正常，而且要讓大家注意到你很渴望成功。

IV. 填空：

　　In order to succeed, you must ___1___ your skills. ___2___ your talents by getting really good at something. ___3___ your thinking by staying current with the latest trends.

　　More importantly, ___4___ your passion with positive energy. ___5___ your talent like a growing tree. Once you put all this together, you can ___6___ a better deal.

　　Likewise, have a ___7___ appearance. Act like a ___8___ person, but make yourself ___9___ to others.

　　為了要成功，你必須精通你的專業技術。要藉由非常精通某事，來運用你的才能。要跟上最新的趨勢，讓你的想法跟得上時代。

　　更重要的是，要用正能量來培養你的熱情。要培養你的才能，讓它像樹一樣成長、茁壯。一旦你將這些全部加在一起，你就可以協商出一個較好的交易。

　　同樣地，外表要整潔。舉止要像一個中規中矩的人，但要讓自己引人注目。

【解答】 1. master　　2. Mobilize　　3. Modernize　　4. nourish
　　　　 5. Nurture　　6. negotiate　　7. neat　　8. normal
　　　　 9. noticeable

　　＊ current〔ˋkɝənt〕*adj.* 現在的；當前的
　　　 stay current with the latest trends 跟得上最新的趨勢

V. 詞彙題：

Directions: *Choose the one word that best completes the sentence.*

1. Success will come once you've _____ your skills.
   (A) melted　(B) mastered　(C) mentioned　(D) monitored

2. _____ your talent by putting it to good use.
   (A) Meditate　(B) Mobilize　(C) Mourn　(D) Mock

3. We must constantly _____ our thinking.
   (A) minimize　(B) multiply　(C) modernize　(D) mumble

4. _____ your talents with constant practice.
   (A) Notify　(B) Nag　(C) Nourish　(D) Nibble

5. _____ your passion with dedication.
   (A) Notice　(B) Nominate　(C) Narrate　(D) Nurture

6. Learn how to _____ a better deal.
   (A) negotiate　(B) nominate　(C) navigate　(D) neglect

7. Be professional and maintain a _____ appearance.
   (A) neat　(B) nasty　(C) numerous　(D) nervous

8. Try to act like a _____ person no matter what happens.
   (A) narrow　(B) nutritious　(C) nuclear　(D) normal

9. Make your enthusiasm _____ to those around you.
   (A) nearsighted　(B) negative　(C) naughty　(D) noticeable

【答案】1.（B）　2.（B）　3.（C）　4.（C）　5.（D）　6.（A）
　　　　7.（A）　8.（D）　9.（D）

VI. 同義字整理：

1. **master** 〔ˈmæstɚ〕 v. 精通
   - = learn 〔lɝn〕
   - = understand 〔ˌʌndɚˈstænd〕
   - = acquire 〔əˈkwaɪr〕

   - = grasp 〔græsp〕
   - = pick up

2. **mobilize** 〔ˈmoblˌaɪz〕 v. 動員
   - = deploy 〔dɪˈplɔɪ〕
   - = prepare 〔prɪˈpɛr〕
   - = organize 〔ˈɔrgənˌaɪz〕

3. **modernize** 〔ˈmadɚnˌaɪz〕 v. 使現代化
   - = update 〔ʌpˈdet〕
   - = renew 〔rɪˈnju〕
   - = remake 〔riˈmek〕

4. **nourish** 〔ˈnɝɪʃ〕 v. 滋養
   - = feed 〔fid〕
   - = nurture 〔ˈnɝtʃɚ〕
   - = cultivate 〔ˈkʌltəˌvet〕
   - = encourage 〔ɪnˈkɝɪdʒ〕

5. **nurture** 〔ˈnɝtʃɚ〕 v. 養育
   - = develop 〔dɪˈvɛləp〕
   - = grow 〔gro〕
   - = cultivate 〔ˈkʌltəˌvet〕

6. **negotiate** 〔nɪˈgoʃɪˌet〕 v. 談判；協商
   - = bargain 〔ˈbargɪn〕
   - = deal 〔dil〕
   - = discuss 〔dɪˈskʌs〕

7. **neat** 〔nit〕 adj. 整潔的
   - = tidy 〔ˈtaɪdɪ〕
   - = organized 〔ˈɔrgənˌaɪzd〕
   - = clean 〔klin〕

8. **normal** 〔ˈnɔrmḷ〕 adj. 正常的
   - = modest 〔ˈmadɪst〕
   - = unassuming 〔ˌʌnəˈsjumɪŋ〕
   - = regular 〔ˈrɛgjələ〕

9. **noticeable** 〔ˈnotɪsəbḷ〕 adj. 顯著的；明顯的
   - = outstanding 〔ˈautˈstændɪŋ〕
   - = striking 〔ˈstraɪkɪŋ〕
   - = bold 〔bold〕

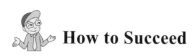

How to Succeed

16. O

看英文唸出中文	一口氣說九句	看中文唸出英文
obey[2] 〔əˋbe〕v.	*Obey*. 要服從。	服從；遵守
order[1] 〔ˋɔrdɚ〕n.	Follow *orders*. 要遵照命令。	命令
opportunity[3] 〔͵ɑpɚˋtjunətɪ〕n.	Seek *opportunities*. 要尋求機會。	機會

offer[2] 〔ˋɔfɚ〕v.	*Offer*. 要提供協助。	提供
overcome[4] 〔͵ovɚˋkʌm〕v.	*Overcome*. 要克服一切。	克服
obliging[6] 〔əˋblaɪdʒɪŋ〕adj.	Be *obliging*. 要樂於助人。	樂於助人的； 親切的

outright[6] 〔ˋaʊt͵raɪt〕adj.	*Outright*. 要直率。	直率的
optimistic[3] 〔͵ɑptəˋmɪstɪk〕adj.	*Optimistic*. 要樂觀。	樂觀的
outstanding[4] 〔ˋaʊtˋstændɪŋ〕adj.	*Outstanding*. 要傑出。	傑出的

I. 背景説明：

Obey.（要服從。）*Obey* authority.（要服從上級。）【authority〔ə'θɔrətɪ〕*n.* 權威；管理機構】*Obey* the rules.（要遵守規定。）*Obey* the law.（要遵守法律。）*Follow orders.*（要遵照命令。）有些人做不到時，會更改命令，讓自己和公司都受到損害。Execute the *order.*（要執行命令。）*Seek opportunities.*（要尋求機會。）可説成：*Seek* more *opportunites.*（要尋求更多的機會。）*Seek opportunities* to advance.（要尋求進步的機會。）

Obey.
Follow orders.
Seek opportunities.

Offer.（要提供協助。）（= *Offer to help.*）可説成：*Offer* to be of assistance.（要提供協助。）*Overcome.*（要克服一切。）（= *Overcome everything.*）可説成：*Overcome* your anxiety.（要克服你的焦慮。）*Overcome* your fear.（要克服你的恐懼。）*Be obliging.*（要樂於助人。）（= *Be willing to help others.*）不要和 Be obliged.（要懂得感謝。）搞混。

Outright.（要直率。）可説成：Be *outright.*（要直率。）（= *Be blunt.* = *Be straightforward.*）*Optimistic.*（要樂觀。）（= *Be optimistic.*）Have an *optimistic* outlook.（要有樂觀的看法。）*Outstanding.*（要傑出。）（= *Be outstanding.*）可説成：Be *outstanding* in your field.（在你的領域要傑出。）Have an *outstanding* attitude.（要有超好的態度。）

II. 英語演講：

【一字英語演講】	【短篇英語演講】
Teachers, students, and parents:	*Teachers, students, and parents:* 各位老師、同學，和家長：
Obey. *Follow orders.* *Seek opportunities.*	*Obey* the rules. 要遵守所有的規定。 *Follow* all *orders*. 要遵照命令。 *Seek* more *opportunities*. 要尋求更多的機會。
Offer. *Overcome.* *Be obliging.*	*Offer* to help. 要提供協助。 *Overcome* your anxiety. 要克服你的焦慮。 *Be obliging* to everyone. 要樂於助人。
Outright. *Optimistic.* *Outstanding.*	Be *outright* in thought and action. 思想和行為都要直率。 Be *optimistic* and positive. 要非常樂觀。 Be an *outstanding* individual. 要做一個傑出的人。
You will achieve success.	*You will achieve success.* 你一定會成功。

III. 短篇作文：

How to Achieve Success

To achieve success, you will have to *overcome* a number of challenges. *Most of all*, you'll need to *obey* the rules and *follow* all *orders*. *Seek* more *opportunities*. *In fact*, it's also important to have an *optimistic* attitude, and *be obliging* to others. *Offer* to be of assistance. Be *outright* in thought and action. Only then can you be an *outstanding* individual.

如何成功

要成功，你必須克服許多挑戰。最重要的是，你必須遵守規定，並遵照所有的命令。要尋求更多的機會。事實上，有樂觀的態度，並且熱心助人，也是很重要的。要願意提供協助。思想和言行都要直率。只有到那時候，你才能成為一個傑出的人。

* assistance〔ə'sɪstəns〕*n.* 協助

IV. 填空：

In order to succeed, first, you must ___1___ authority. Next, you must follow ___2___. Finally, you can seize ___3___.

In addition to that, you should always ___4___ to help. In this way, you can ___5___ your anxiety. A successful person is ___6___ to everyone.

Likewise, be ___7___ in thought and action. Be ___8___ and positive. Then you'll be an ___9___ individual.

為了要成功，首先，你必須服從上級。其次，你必須遵照命令。最後，你就可以抓住機會。

此外，你應該總是提供協助。如此一來，你就可以克服你的焦慮。成功的人會樂於助人。

同樣地，思想和行為都要直率。要非常樂觀。那樣你就會是個傑出的人。

【解答】 1. obey　2. orders　3. opportunities　4. offer
　　　　5. overcome　6. obliging　7. outright　8. optimistic
　　　　9. outstanding

* anxiety〔æŋ'zaɪətɪ〕*n.* 焦慮

V. 詞彙題：

Directions: *Choose the one word that best completes the sentence.*

1. Be smart and _____ the rules.
   (A) offend　(B) obtain　(C) obey　(D) occupy

2. Memorize your _____ and execute them to the best of your ability.
   (A) organs　(B) orders　(C) occasions　(D) obstacles

3. Don't hesitate to seize an _____ to advance.
   (A) opportunity　(B) orchestra　(C) overpass　(D) operation

4. Win friends and allies by _____ to help others.
   (A) opposing　(B) oppressing　(C) omitting　(D) offering

5. Train your mind to _____ anxiety.
   (A) overcome　(B) originate　(C) object　(D) organize

6. Earn people's trust with an _____ attitude.
   (A) organic　(B) opposite　(C) obliging　(D) optional

7. Be _____ in both thought and action.
   (A) occasional　(B) outright　(C) obscure　(D) outdoor

8. An _____ person sees the good that may come.
   (A) official　(B) offensive　(C) operational　(D) optimistic

9. You will be rewarded for your _____ achievements.
   (A) outstanding　(B) outgoing　(C) obstinate　(D) orderly

【答案】 1.(C)　2.(B)　3.(A)　4.(D)　5.(A)　6.(C)
　　　　 7.(B)　8.(D)　9.(A)

VI. 同義字整理 :

1. **obey**〔ə'be〕v. 服從；遵守
   = follow〔'fɑlo〕
   = observe〔əb'zɝv〕
   = comply with

2. **follow orders** 要遵照命令
   = follow directions
   = follow commands
   = obey instructions

3. **seek opportunities** 要尋
   求機會
   = seek openings
   = seek breaks
   = look for chances

4. **offer**〔'ɔfɚ〕v. 提供
   = provide〔prə'vaɪd〕
   = present〔prɪ'zɛnt〕
   = volunteer〔,vɑlən'tɪr〕

5. **overcome**〔,ovɚ'kʌm〕v.
   克服
   = conquer〔'kɑŋkɚ〕
   = defeat〔dɪ'fit〕
   = master〔'mæstɚ〕

6. **obliging**〔ə'blaɪdʒɪŋ〕adj. 樂於
   助人的；親切的
   = accommodating
     〔ə'kɑmə,detɪŋ〕
   = friendly〔'frɛndlɪ〕
   = cooperative〔ko'ɑpə,retɪv〕
   = helpful〔'hɛlpfəl〕

7. **outright**〔'aʊt,raɪt〕adj. 直率的
   = direct〔də'rɛkt〕
   = certain〔'sɝtn̩〕
   = straightforward
     〔,stret'fɔrwəd〕

8. **optimistic**〔,ɑptə'mɪstɪk〕adj.
   樂觀的
   = hopeful〔'hopfəl〕
   = positive〔'pɑzətɪv〕
   = confident〔'kɑnfədənt〕

9. **outstanding**〔'aʊt'stændɪŋ〕adj.
   傑出的
   = impressive〔ɪm'prɛsɪv〕
   = distinguished〔dɪ'stɪŋgwɪʃt〕
   = exceptional〔ɪk'sɛpʃən̩〕

How to Succeed

17. P

看英文唸出中文	一口氣說九句	看中文唸出英文
plan[1] 〔 plæn 〕 v.	*Plan*. 要計劃。	計劃
prepare[1] 〔 prɪ'pɛr 〕 v.	字首是 Pr { *Prepare*. 要準備。	準備
produce[2] 〔 prə'djus 〕 v.	*Produce*. 要有生產力。	生產
persist[5] 〔 pɚ'sɪst 〕 v.	*Persist*. 要堅持。	堅持;持續
persevere[6] 〔 ˌpɝsə'vɪr 〕 v.	字首都是 Per { *Persevere*. 要不屈不撓。	堅忍;不屈不撓
perceive[5] 〔 pɚ'siv 〕 v.	*Perceive*. 要眼觀 四面,耳聽八方。	察覺;感覺
participate[3] 〔 par'tɪsəˌpet 〕 v.	*Participate*. 要參與。	參加
positive[2] 〔 'pazətɪv 〕 adj.	字首都是 p { Be *positive*. 要正面思考。 都有 /a/ 的音	樂觀的;正面的
patient[2] 〔 'peʃənt 〕 adj.	Be *patient*. 要有耐心。	有耐心的

I. 背景說明：

　　Plan.（要計劃。）可說成：*Plan* ahead.（要預先計劃。）*Plan* wisely.（要聰明地計劃。）*Prepare*.（要準備。）(= *Be prepared*.) 可說成：*Prepare* yourself.（自己要準備好。）*Prepare* for the best outcome.（要準備迎接最好的結果。）(= *Be ready for good things*. = *Be optimistic*.) 有句諺語是：Hope for the best and *prepare* for the worst.（要有最好的打算和做最壞的準備。）*Produce*.（要有生產力。）*Produce* results.（要產生效果。）Be a top *producer*.（要做一個最有生產力的人。）

　　Persist.（要堅持。）(= *Be persistent*.) *Persist* when the going gets tough.（當情況不好時，要堅持。）【*the going* 進展；情況】*Persevere*.（要不屈不撓。）*Persevere* through hardship.（遇到困難要不屈不撓。）*Persevere* in the face of danger.（面對危險要堅忍。）*Perceive*.（要眼觀四面，耳聽八方。）做一個成功者，要感覺到他人的意圖。(*Perceive others' intentions*.) perceive 是感官動詞，意思是「聽到或看到」，即是「察覺；感覺」。

　　Participate.（要參與。）想要成功，什麼都要參與，要有參與的渴望。(*Be eager to participate*.) *Participate* in all activities.（要參加所有的活動。）*Be positive*.（要正面思考。）(= *Be optimistic*.) Have a *positive* attitude.（要有正面的態度。）*Be patient*.（要有耐心。）可加長為：*Be patient* with others.（對別人要有耐心。）

Ⅱ. 英語演講：

【一字英語演講】

Here's some advice:

Plan.
Prepare.
Produce.

Persist.
Persevere.
Perceive.

Participate.
Be positive.
Be patient.

That's how you achieve success.

【短篇英語演講】

Here's some advice: 以下是一些建議：

Plan ahead. 要預先計劃。
Prepare yourself. 自己要準備好。
Produce results. 要產生效果。

Persist when the going gets tough.
當情況不好時，要堅持。
Persevere through hardship.
遇到困難要不屈不撓。
Perceive others' intentions.
要感覺到他人的意圖。

Be eager to *participate*. 要有參與的渴望。
Have a *positive* attitude. 要有正面的態度。
Be patient with others. 對別人要有耐心。

That's how you achieve success.
那就是你的成功之道。

Ⅲ. 短篇作文：

Methods to Succeed

If you *plan* wisely, success is assured. If you maintain a *positive* outlook and remain *patient* with people, you can *prepare* for the best outcome. *Produce* results. *Persist* when the going gets tough. *Persevere* in the face of danger. *Perceive* others' intentions. *Participate* in all activities. *In the end*, you will achieve success.

成功的方法

　　如果你聰明地計劃，就一定會成功。如果你保持樂觀的看法，並一直對人有耐心，你就可以準備迎接最好的結果。要產生效果。當情況不好時，要堅持。面對危險要堅忍。要感覺到他人的意圖。要參加所有的活動。最後，你一定會成功。

IV. 填空：

　　Successful people always ___1___ ahead. They ___2___ for the worst yet hope for the best. This is how they ___3___ results.

　　First, ___4___ when the going gets tough. Next, ___5___ through hardship. And of course, ___6___ what needs to be done, and just do it.

　　More importantly, be eager to ___7___ in all activities. Have a ___8___ attitude. Be ___9___ with others.

　　成功的人總是會預先計劃。他們會做最壞的準備，但會有最好的打算。以下是他們產生效果的方法。

　　首先，當情況不好時，要堅持。其次，遇到困難要不屈不撓。而且當然，要察覺需要做什麼，而且趕快去做。

　　更重要的是，要渴望參與所有的活動。要有正面的態度。對別人要有耐心。

【解答】 1. plan　 2. prepare　 3. produce　 4. persist
　　　　 5. persevere　 6. perceive　 7. participate
　　　　 8. positive　 9. patient
　　　* ahead〔əˋhɛd〕 *adv.* 預先；事前　　 tough〔tʌf〕 *adj.* 艱難的

V. 詞彙題：

Directions: *Choose the one word that best completes the sentence.*

1. Get in the habit of _____ ahead.
   (A) paralyzing　(B) perishing　(C) planning　(D) poaching

2. _____ for the worst and hope for the best.
   (A) Polish　(B) Prepare　(C) Pollute　(D) Postpone

3. Don't spend your time talking; _____ results.
   (A) promise　(B) predict　(C) pretend　(D) produce

4. You must _____ despite failure.
   (A) persist　(B) preview　(C) prefer　(D) prosper

5. Find the inner strength to _____ through hardship.
   (A) provoke　(B) publish　(C) persevere　(D) preserve

6. Use your insight to _____ difficulties ahead.
   (A) perceive　(B) publicize　(C) prolong　(D) puzzle

7. Be eager to _____ in all that life has to offer.
   (A) punch　(B) protest　(C) participate　(D) prosecute

8. A _____ attitude will serve you better than anger.
   (A) punctual　(B) profitable　(C) pregnant　(D) positive

9. Be _____ with others less fortunate than yourself.
   (A) private　(B) patient　(C) productive　(D) preventive

【答案】1.（C）　2.（B）　3.（D）　4.（A）　5.（C）　6.（A）
　　　　7.（C）　8.（D）　9.（B）

VI. 同義字整理：

1. **plan** 〔 plæn 〕 *v.* 計劃
   - = devise 〔 dɪ'vaɪz 〕
   - = organize 〔'ɔrgən,aɪz 〕
   - = arrange 〔 ə'rendʒ 〕
   - = invent 〔 ɪn'vɛnt 〕

2. **prepare** 〔 prɪ'pɛr 〕 *v.* 準備
   - = plan 〔 plæn 〕
   - = anticipate 〔 æn'tɪsə,pet 〕
   - = get ready

3. **produce** 〔 prə'djus 〕 *v.* 生產
   - = make 〔 mek 〕
   - = build 〔 bɪld 〕
   - = create 〔 krɪ'et 〕
   - = develop 〔 dɪ'vɛləp 〕

4. **persist** 〔 pɚ'sɪst 〕 *v.* 堅持；持續
   - = endure 〔 ɪn'djur 〕
   - = persevere 〔,pɝsə'vɪr 〕
   - = continue 〔 kən'tɪnju 〕
   - = go on

5. **persevere** 〔,pɝsə'vɪr 〕 *v.* 堅忍；不屈不撓
   - = persist 〔 pɚ'sɪst 〕
   - = continue 〔 kən'tɪnju 〕
   - = remain firm

6. **perceive** 〔 pɚ'siv 〕 *v.* 察覺；感覺
   - = see 〔 si 〕
   - = notice 〔'notɪs 〕
   - = understand 〔,ʌndɚ'stænd 〕

7. **participate** 〔 par'tɪsə,pet 〕 *v.* 參加
   - = take part
   - = join 〔 dʒɔɪn 〕
   - = be engaged

8. **positive** 〔'pazətɪv 〕 *adj.* 樂觀的；正面的
   - = optimistic 〔,aptə'mɪstɪk 〕
   - = hopeful 〔'hopfəl 〕
   - = encouraging 〔 ɪn'kɝɪdʒɪŋ 〕

9. **patient** 〔'peʃənt 〕 *adj.* 有耐心的
   - = understanding 〔,ʌndɚ'stændɪŋ 〕
   - = forgiving 〔 fɚ'gɪvɪŋ 〕
   - = tolerant 〔'talərənt 〕

How to Succeed

18. R (1)

看英文唸出中文	一口氣說九句	看中文唸出英文
respect[2] 〔 rɪ'spɛkt 〕*v.*	字首都是 Re	*Respect*. 要尊敬別人。	尊敬
remain[3] 〔 rɪ'men 〕*v.*		*Remain*. 要保持得住。	保持
resolve[4] 〔 rɪ'zɑlv 〕*v.*		*Resolve*. 要有決心。	決心

reform[4] 〔 rɪ'fɔrm 〕*v.*	字首都是 Re	*Reform*. 要改革。	改革
regard[2] 〔 rɪ'gɑrd 〕*v.*		*Regard*. 要尊重他人。	認爲；尊重
reinforce[6] 〔 ˌriɪn'fors 〕*v.*		*Reinforce*. 要加強好的行爲。	增強

require[2] 〔 rɪ'kwaɪr 〕*v.*	字首是 Requ	*Require*. 要要求。	需要；要求
request[3] 〔 rɪ'kwɛst 〕*v.*		*Request*. 要請求。	請求
realize[2] 〔 'rɪəˌlaɪz 〕*v.*		*Realize* your dream. 要實現你的夢想。	實現

I. 背景説明：

Respect.（要尊敬別人。）(= *Respect others*.) ***Respect***
yourself.（要重視自己。）(= *Take care of yourself*.) <u>re¦ spect</u> 眼
                                              again¦ look
睛不停地看，即是「重視」和「尊敬」。做一個成功者，連對自己最
親近的人都要尊敬。*Remain*.（要保持得住。）在這裡是指「要保持
冷靜。」(*Remain calm*.)、「要保持樂觀。」(= *Remain optimistic*.)
Resolve.（要有決心。）***Resolve*** to succeed.（要決心成功。）
Resolve to be excellent.（要決心做到最好。）

Reform.（要改革。）(= *Improve*.) ***Reform*** your plan.（要改
良你的計劃。）不能説計劃訂了就不改。***Reform*** the situation.
（要改善情況。）(= *Improve the situation*.) *Regard*.（要尊重他
人。）***Regard*** others highly.（要很尊敬他人。）***Regard*** others
with kindness.（要敬愛他人。）regard 還可作「認為」解
(= *consider*)。***Regard*** your work as precious.（要認為你的工作
很珍貴。）*Reinforce*.（要加強。）***Reinforce*** good behavior.（要
加強好的行為。）***Reinforce*** positive habits.（要加強好的習慣。）

Require.（要要求。）***Require*** obedience.（要要求服從。）
Require precision.（要要求精確。）*Request*.（要請求。）***Request***
information.（要請求提供資訊。）***Request*** more work.（要請求更
多的工作量。）*Realize your dream*.（要實現你的夢想。）可説成：
Realize your ambitions.（要實現你的抱負。）***Realize*** your goals.
（要實現你的目標。）

這一回的九句話，全部是 Re 開頭，唸一遍就記得。不停地唸
「成功勵志經」，無形中會改變自己的心態，邁向成功。

II. 英語演講：

【一字英語演講】

Friends and associates:

Respect.
Remain.
Resolve.

Reform.
Regard.
Reinforce.

Require.
Request.
Realize your dream.

Success is assured.

【短篇英語演講】

Friends and associates: 各位朋友，各位同事：

Respect others. 要尊敬別人。
Remain calm. 要保持冷靜。
Resolve to succeed. 要決心成功。

Reform your outlook. 要改善你的看法。
Regard others highly. 要很尊敬他人。
Reinforce good behavior. 要加強好的行為。

Do what the job *requires*.
要符合工作的要求。
Request information. 要請求提供資訊。
Realize your dream. 要實現你的夢想。

Success is assured. 你一定會成功。

III. 短篇作文：

Advice to Succeed

We all want success, but we frequently need guidance to achieve it. Here are some ways to get started: *Respect* yourself, *remain* optimistic, and *resolve* to be excellent. *Regard* others highly, *reinforce* good behavior, and *reform* the situation. *Finally*, *require* precision, *request* more work, and *realize* your ambitions.

成功的建議

我們都想要成功，但是我們常需要人指導，才能成功。以下是一些方法，能讓你開始：要重視自己、保持樂觀，並要決心做到最好。要很尊敬他人、加強好的行為，並且改善情況。最後，要要求精確、請求更多的工作量，並且要實現你的抱負。

* guidance〔ˈgaɪdəns〕 *n.* 指導　　ambition〔æmˈbɪʃən〕 *n.* 抱負

IV. 填空：

　　Success comes in a variety of forms but it never comes unless you ___1___ yourself and others. By ___2___ calm and optimistic, you can ___3___ to achieve something great.

　　Additionally, you can ___4___ a situation with your words. Successful people always ___5___ others highly. You have to ___6___ a positive message.

　　In closing, do what the job ___7___ and ___8___ the right information at the right time. Then you can ___9___ your dream.

　　成功有各種不同的形式，但是除非你重視自己並尊敬他人，成功是不會來臨的。藉由保持冷靜和樂觀，你可以決心達成很棒的事。

　　此外，你可以用言語改善情況。成功的人總是很尊敬他人。你必須加強正面的訊息。

　　總之，要符合工作的要求，並在適當的時候，請求提供正確的資訊。那樣你就能實現你的夢想。

【解答】 1. respect　2. remaining　3. resolve　4. reform
　　　　　5. regard　6. reinforce　7. requires　8. request
　　　　　9. realize
　　　　　* *come in* 有…　　*a variety of* 各種不同的
　　　　　in closing 總之

V. 詞彙題：

Directions: *Choose the one word that best completes the sentence.*

1. Be your own person but _____ others' viewpoints.
   (A) relax　(B) resent　(C) rescue　(D) respect

2. No matter what happens, _____ calm.
   (A) remove　(B) reply　(C) remain　(D) release

3. Look deep inside yourself and _____ to succeed.
   (A) resolve　(B) relay　(C) reject　(D) refute

4. Never be afraid to _____ your outlook.
   (A) refund　(B) reform　(C) rehearse　(D) relate

5. It costs nothing to _____ others with kindness.
   (A) regard　(B) reflect　(C) recycle　(D) recover

6. A good leader knows how to _____ good behavior.
   (A) recall　(B) reconcile　(C) reinforce　(D) rebel

7. Be willing to do whatever the job _____.
   (A) repeats　(B) relieves　(C) repairs　(D) requires

8. _____ information from those in the know.
   (A) Represent　(B) Resign　(C) Request　(D) Restrain

9. Have the courage to _____ your wildest dreams.
   (A) realize　(B) retreat　(C) resemble　(D) retaliate

【答案】 1.（D）　2.（C）　3.（A）　4.（B）　5.（A）　6.（C）
　　　　 7.（D）　8.（C）　9.（A）

VI. 同義字整理：

1. **respect** 〔 rɪ'spɛkt 〕 *v.* 尊敬
   - = regard 〔 rɪ'gɑrd 〕
   - = esteem 〔 ə'stim 〕
   - = revere 〔 rɪ'vɪr 〕
   - = look up to

2. **remain** 〔 rɪ'men 〕 *v.* 保持
   - = stay 〔 ste 〕
   - = endure 〔 ɪn'djʊr 〕
   - = continue 〔 kən'tɪnjʊ 〕
   - = persist 〔 pɚ'sɪst 〕

3. **resolve** 〔 rɪ'zɑlv 〕 *v.* 決心
   - = determine 〔 dɪ't͡ɜmɪn 〕
   - = decide 〔 dɪ'saɪd 〕

4. **reform** 〔 rɪ'fɔrm 〕 *v.* 改革
   - = modify 〔 'mɑdə,faɪ 〕
   - = remake 〔 ri'mek 〕
   - = improve 〔 ɪm'pruv 〕

5. **regard** 〔 rɪ'gɑrd 〕 *v.* ①認爲 ②尊重
   - ① = consider 〔 kən'sɪdɚ 〕
     = judge 〔 dʒʌdʒ 〕
   - ② = respect 〔 rɪ'spɛkt 〕
     = esteem 〔 ə'stim 〕

6. **reinforce** 〔 ,riɪn'fors 〕 *v.* 增強
   - = encourage 〔 ɪn'kɝɪdʒ 〕
   - = support 〔 sə'port 〕
   - = fortify 〔 'fɔrtə,faɪ 〕

7. **require** 〔 rɪ'kwaɪr 〕 *v.* 需要；要求
   - = need 〔 nid 〕
   - = demand 〔 dɪ'mænd 〕
   - = depend upon

8. **request** 〔 rɪ'kwɛst 〕 *v.* 請求
   - = ask for
   - = call for
   - = seek 〔 sik 〕

9. **realize** 〔 'riə,laɪz 〕 *v.* 實現
   - = achieve 〔 ə'tʃiv 〕
   - = accomplish 〔 ə'kɑmplɪʃ 〕
   - = fulfill 〔 fʊl'fɪl 〕
   - = make real

How to Succeed

19. R (2)

看英文唸出中文	一口氣說九句	看中文唸出英文
react³ 〔 rɪˋækt 〕 v. relax³ 〔 rɪˋlæks 〕 v. revive⁵ 〔 rɪˋvaɪv 〕 v.	字首都是 Re { *React*. 要有反應。 *Relax*. 要放輕鬆。 *Revive*. 要能恢復精神。 都有 /æ/ 的音 ＊放輕鬆後，才能恢復精神。	反應 放鬆 復活
refine⁶ 〔 rɪˋfaɪn 〕 v. renew³ 〔 rɪˋnju 〕 v. rejoice⁵ 〔 rɪˋdʒɔɪs 〕 v.	字首都是 Re { *Refine*. 要改進。 *Renew*. 要更新。 *Rejoice*. 要高高興興。 意思相近	精煉；改進 更新；恢復 高興
rapid² 〔 ˋræpɪd 〕 adj. radiant⁶ 〔 ˋredɪənt 〕 adj. robust⁵ 〔 roˋbʌst 〕 adj.	字首是 ra { Be *rapid*. 要快速。 *Radiant*. 要容光煥發。 *Robust*. 要強健。 字尾是 t	快速的 容光煥發的 強健的

I. 背景説明：

React.（要有反應。）在公司上班，對公司要求的事情，要有反應，否則就不被人重視，無法成功。*React* at the right time.（要在對的時間做出反應。）*React* immediately.（要立刻反應。）*React* in an appropriate way.（要用適當的方式反應。）不論贊成或不贊成，態度很重要。*Relax*.（要放輕鬆。）（= *Be relaxed*.）*Rexlax* when your work is finished.（工作做完時，要放輕鬆。）Don't *relax* on the job.（工作不要鬆懈。）No matter what happens, just *relax*.（無論發生什麼事，都要放輕鬆。）*Revive*.（要能恢復精神。）（= *Revive yourself*.）*Revive* your enthusiasm.（要恢復你的熱忱。）

Refine.（要改進。）*Refine* your talents.（要讓你的能力更進步。）*Refine* your knowledge.（要讓你的知識更豐富。）*Renew*.（要更新。）*Renew* your desire to succeed.（要恢復你想要成功的渴望。）*Renew* your strategy.（要更新你的策略。）*Rejoice*.（要高高興興。）*Rejoice* for others.（要為他人高興。）*Rejoice* for your own success.（要為自己的成功高興。）背 rejoice 這個字，可以先背人名 Joyce（喬依思），不要和 joy〔dʒɔɪ〕*n.* 高興 搞混。

Be rapid.（要快速。）Move at a *rapid* pace.（步調要快。）Be a *rapid* thinker.（腦筋要動得快。）*Radiant*.（要容光煥發。）（= *Be radiant*.）Have a *radiant* smile.（要有燦爛的微笑。）*Robust*.（要強健。）（= *Be robust*. = *Be strong and healthy*.）Be a *robust* worker.（要做一個強健的工作者。）

II. 英語演講：

【一字英語演講】	【短篇英語演講】
Students:	*Students:* 同學們：
React.	*React* in an appropriate way.
Relax.	要用適當的方式反應。
Revive.	No matter what happens, just *relax*.
	無論發生什麼事，都要放輕鬆。
Refine.	*Revive* your passion. 要恢復你的熱情。
Renew.	
Rejoice.	*Refine* your talents. 要讓你的能力更進步。
	Renew your enthusiasm. 要恢復你的熱忱。
Be rapid.	*Rejoice* for others. 要為他人高興。
Radiant.	
Robust.	*Be* a *rapid* thinker. 腦筋要動得快。
	Have a *radiant* smile. 要有燦爛的微笑。
Success is coming	Be a *robust* worker. 要做一個強健的工作者。
to you.	
	Success is coming to you. 你會成功的。

III. 短篇作文：

Steps to Success

There's a nine-step blueprint for success. Step 1: *React* to situations in an appropriate way. Step 2: No matter what happens, just *relax*. Step 3: *Revive* your enthusiasm for your work each and every morning. Step 4: *Refine* your knowledge. Step 5: *Renew* your commitment to the goal. Step 6: *Rejoice* for every opportunity. Step 7: Move at a *rapid* pace. Step 8: Have a *radiant* smile. *And finally*, step 9: Be a *robust* worker who never gets tired.

成功的步驟

　　成功的藍圖有九個步驟。第一步：要以適當的方式對情況做出反應。第二步：無論發生什麼事，都要放輕鬆。第三步：每天早上都要恢復你對工作的熱忱。第四步：要讓你的知識更豐富。第五步：要恢復你對目標的熱情。第六步：要為每個機會感到高興。第七步，步調要快。第八步：要有燦爛的微笑。最後，第九步：要做一個孜孜不倦的強健工作者。

　　each and every 每個　　commitment〔kə'mɪtmənt〕*n.* 熱情；決心

IV. 填空：

　　To achieve success, you must ___1___ in an appropriate way. Don't ___2___ until the job is done right. ___3___ your passion each and every day.

　　Likewise, ___4___ your talents and increase your value. ___5___ your enthusiasm for achieving success. ___6___ for others when they accomplish their goals.

　　Moreover, be a ___7___ thinker. Have a ___8___ smile. Be a ___9___ worker who never gets tired.

　　想要成功，你必須用適當的方式反應。直到工作做好之前，都不要鬆懈。每一天都要恢復你的熱情。

　　同樣地，要讓你的能力更進步，並增加你的價值。要恢復你想要成功的熱忱。當別人達成目標時，要為他們高興。

　　此外，腦筋要動得快。要有燦爛的微笑。要成為一個孜孜不倦的強健工作者。

【解答】 1. react　2. relax　3. Revive　4. refine　5. Renew
　　　　　6. Rejoice　7. rapid　8. radiant　9. robust

　　　＊ appropriate〔ə'proprɪɪt〕*adj.* 適當的

V. 詞彙題：

Directions: *Choose the one word that best completes the sentence.*

1. Assess the situation and _____ appropriately.
   (A) react　(B) recur　(C) reside　(D) revive

2. Instead of panicking, just _____.
   (A) resort　(B) roast　(C) rotate　(D) relax

3. Develop a routine to _____ your spirits.
   (A) regret　(B) revive　(C) refuse　(D) recruit

4. Constantly practice the simple things, _____ your skills.
   (A) reducing　(B) responding　(C) refining　(D) retorting

5. Taking an oath will _____ your commitment to a project.
   (A) renew　(B) ridicule　(C) rhyme　(D) ruin

6. You can _____ only after reaching the goal.
   (A) rumble　(B) rustle　(C) rejoice　(D) recognize

7. Be a _____ thinker and quick on your feet.
   (A) rough　(B) rapid　(C) reluctant　(D) remote

8. Show everybody that _____ smile.
   (A) reckless　(B) reliable　(C) relevant　(D) radiant

9. A _____ person is difficult to keep down.
   (A) robust　(B) respective　(C) ragged　(D) rural

【答案】1.（A）　2.（D）　3.（B）　4.（C）　5.（A）　6.（C）
　　　　7.（B）　8.（D）　9.（A）

VI. 同義字整理：

1. **react**〔rɪˈækt〕*v.* 反應
   = respond〔rɪˈspɑnd〕
   = act〔ækt〕
   = proceed〔prəˈsid〕

2. **relax**〔rɪˈlæks〕*v.* 放鬆
   = calm down
   = take it easy
   = loosen up

3. **revive**〔rɪˈvaɪv〕*v.* 復活
   = renew〔rɪˈnju〕
   = revitalize〔riˈvaɪtḷˌaɪz〕
   = restore〔rɪˈstor〕

4. **refine**〔rɪˈfaɪn〕*v.* 精煉；
   改進
   = improve〔ɪmˈpruv〕
   = perfect〔pɚˈfɛkt〕
   = polish〔ˈpɑlɪʃ〕

5. **renew**〔rɪˈnju〕*v.* 更新；恢復
   = reaffirm〔ˌriəˈfɝm〕
   = regenerate〔rɪˈdʒɛnəˌret〕
   = rejuvenate〔rɪˈdʒuvəˌnet〕
   = continue〔kənˈtɪnju〕

6. **rejoice**〔rɪˈdʒɔɪs〕*v.* 高興
   = celebrate〔ˈsɛləˌbret〕
   = delight〔dɪˈlaɪt〕
   = be glad
   = be happy

7. **rapid**〔ˈræpɪd〕*adj.* 快速的
   = quick〔kwɪk〕
   = fast〔fæst〕
   = swift〔swɪft〕
   = brisk〔brɪsk〕

8. **radiant**〔ˈredɪənt〕*adj.* 容光
   煥發的
   = glowing〔ˈgloɪŋ〕
   = bright〔braɪt〕
   = brilliant〔ˈbrɪljənt〕

9. **robust**〔roˈbʌst〕*adj.* 強健的
   = healthy〔ˈhɛlθɪ〕
   = vigorous〔ˈvɪgərəs〕
   = hardy〔ˈhɑrdɪ〕

How to Succeed

20. S (1)

看英文唸出中文	一 口 氣 説 九 句	看中文唸出英文
smart[1] 〔 smɑrt 〕 *adj.*	Be *smart*. 要聰明。	聰明的
skilled[2] 〔 skɪld 〕 *adj.*	*Skilled*. 要有專業技術。	熟練的； 有技能的
sophisticated[6] 〔 sə'fɪstɪˌketɪd 〕 *adj.*	*Sophisticated*. 要懂得人情世故。	世故的；老練的
sincere[3] 〔 sɪn'sɪr 〕 *adj.*	*Sincere*. 要眞誠。	眞誠的
strict[2] 〔 strɪkt 〕 *adj.*	*Strict*. 要嚴格。	嚴格的
sympathetic[4] 〔ˌsɪmpə'θɛtɪk 〕 *adj.*	*Sympathetic*. 要有同情心。	同情的
solid[3] 〔'sɑlɪd 〕 *adj.*	*Solid*. 要可靠。	堅固的；可靠的
stable[3] 〔'stebḷ 〕 *adj.*	*Stable*. 要穩定。	穩定的
straightforward[5] 〔ˌstret'fɔrwəd 〕 *adj.*	*Straightforward*. 要直率。	直率的；直接 了當的

字尾是 ed（Skilled / Sophisticated）

字首都是 S（Sincere / Strict / Sympathetic）

字首是 St（Stable / Straightforward）

I. 背景説明：

Be smart. （要聰明。）（ = *Be a smart person.* ）Make *smart* decisions. （要做聰明的決定。）*Skilled.* （要有專業技術。）（ = *Be skilled.* = *Be skillful.* ）Be a *skilled* worker. （要做一個有專業技術的工作者。）unskilled worker 是「沒有專業技術的工作者」，他的工作誰都可以取代，薪水不高。*Sophisticated.* （要懂得人情世故。）（ = *Be sophisticated.* ）Be a *sophisticated* person. （要做一個懂人情世故的人。）

Be smart.
Skilled.
Sophisticated.

Sincere. （要眞誠。）（ = *Be sincere.* ）Be *sincere* in your actions. （你的所做所爲要眞誠。）Be a *sincere* person. （要做一個眞誠的人。）*Strict.* （要嚴格。）（ = *Be strict.* ）Be *strict* about business. （在生意上要嚴格。）*Sympathetic.* （要有同情心。）（ = *Be sympathetic.* ）Be *sympathetic* to others. （對別人要有同情心。）Offer a *sympathetic* ear. （要有同理心來傾聽。）（ = *Be a good listener.* ）

Solid. （要可靠。）（ = *Be solid.* ）Be a *solid* worker. （要做一個可靠的員工。）Build a *solid* character. （要建立實實在在的人格。）*Stable.* （要穩定。）（ = *Be stable.* ）Be *stable* and reliable. （要穩定又可靠。）*Straightforward.* （要直率。）（ = *Be straightforward.* ）Be a *straightforward* talker. （要做一個說話直接了當的人。）

II. 英語演講：

【一字英語演講】	【短篇英語演講】
Boys and girls of all ages:	*Boys and girls of all ages:* 各位男孩和女孩：
	Be smart in everything you do.
Be smart.	做什麼事都要聰明。
Skilled.	Be *skilled* in your field. 要在你的領域具有專業技術。
Sophisticated.	Be a *sophisticated* person. 要做一個懂人情世故的人。
Sincere.	Be *sincere* and genuine. 要非常真誠。
Strict.	Be *strict* about business. 在生意上要嚴格。
Sympathetic.	Offer a *sympathetic* ear. 要有同理心來傾聽。
Solid.	Be a *solid* worker. 要做一個可靠的員工。
Stable.	Be a *stable* friend. 要做一個穩定的朋友。
Straightforward.	Be a *straightforward* talker.
	要做一個說話直接了當的人。
You will be destined for success.	*You will be destined for success.* 你注定會成功。

III. 短篇作文：

Nine Ways to Be a Successful Person

These nine words will bring success. They are: *smart*, *skilled*, *sophisticated*, *sincere*, *strict*, *sympathetic*, *solid*, *stable* and *straightforward*. These words start with the letter "s". *First*, make *smart* choices. Be a *skilled* worker. Be a *sophisticated* person. *Next*, be *sincere*. Be *sympathetic* to others. Be *strict* about business. *Finally*, build a *solid* character. Maintain *stable* relationships. Be a *straightforward* individual.

九個成功的方法

這九個字能帶來成功。它們是：聰明、有專業技術、懂得人情世故、眞誠、嚴格、同情、可靠、穩定，以及直率。這些字的開頭字母都是 "s"。首先，要做聰明的選擇。要做一個有專業技術的工作者。要做一個懂人情世故的人。其次，要眞誠。對別人要有同情心。在生意上要嚴格。最後，要建立實實在在的人格。要維持穩定的關係。要做一個直率的人。

IV. 填空：

     __1__ people always make good decisions. They become __2__ in their profession. They develop a __3__ attitude.

     Therefore, to be successful, you must be __4__ and genuine in words and deeds. That means sometimes you have to be __5__ about doing the right thing. But remember, the most successful people are also __6__ to the needs of others.

     Indeed, a person with a __7__ character is reliable. A __8__ person is someone you can count on; he rarely changes. Success comes when you are __9__ with others. Be direct and honest.

聰明的人總是會做出好的決定。他們在自己的職業具有專業技術。他們會培養圓滑的態度。

因此，爲了要成功，你的言行必須非常眞誠。那就表示，有時候你必須嚴格地做正確的事。但是要記得，最成功的人也會對別人的需求有同理心。

的確，性格實在的人很可靠。穩定的人是你可以依賴的人；他們很少改變。要對別人直率，才會成功。要直接而且誠實。

【解答】 1. Smart   2. skilled   3. sophisticated   4. sincere
     5. strict   6. sympathetic   7. solid   8. stable
     9. straightforward

     * indeed (ɪnˋdid) *adv.* 的確   rarely (ˋrɛrlɪ) *adv.* 很少

V. 詞彙題：

Directions: *Choose the one word that best completes the sentence.*

1. Consider all the options and make _____ decisions.
   (A) smart   (B) salty   (C) sentimental   (D) shady

2. Only the most _____ people rise to the top.
   (A) stale   (B) spiral   (C) skilled   (D) spicy

3. The more you know, the more _____ you will be.
   (A) southern   (B) sophisticated   (C) spare   (D) secondary

4. Everybody likes a _____ and genuine person.
   (A) savage   (B) sincere   (C) scarce   (D) scary

5. Be casual in your personal life, but _____ about your business.
   (A) scenic   (B) selfish   (C) serene   (D) strict

6. Do your best to be a _____ friend.
   (A) shabby   (B) shallow   (C) sympathetic   (D) shameful

7. There is a demand for people with _____ characters.
   (A) solid   (B) shortsighted   (C) skinny   (D) slippery

8. The best friend is a _____ friend.
   (A) sloppy   (B) sneaky   (C) solitary   (D) stable

9. You know what to expect from a _____ talker.
   (A) sufficient   (B) straightforward   (C) symbolic
   (D) synthetic

【答案】1. (A)　2. (C)　3. (B)　4. (B)　5. (D)　6. (C)
　　　　7. (A)　8. (D)　9. (B)

VI. 同義字整理：

1. **smart** 〔 smɑrt 〕 *adj.* 聰明的
   - = intelligent 〔 ɪn'tɛlədʒənt 〕
   - = keen 〔 kin 〕
   - = bright 〔 braɪt 〕

2. **skilled** 〔 skɪld 〕 *adj.* 熟練的；
   有技能的
   - = expert 〔 'ɛkspɜt 〕
   - = professional 〔 prə'fɛʃənḷ 〕
   - = accomplished 〔 ə'kɑmplɪʃt 〕
   - = masterful 〔 'mæstəfəl 〕

3. **sophisticated** 〔 sə'fɪstɪˌketɪd 〕
   adj. 世故的；老練的
   - = refined 〔 rɪ'faɪnd 〕
   - = cultured 〔 'kʌltʃəd 〕
   - = worldly 〔 'wɜldlɪ 〕

4. **sincere** 〔 sɪn'sɪr 〕 *adj.* 眞誠的
   - = genuine 〔 'dʒɛnjuɪn 〕
   - = honest 〔 'ɑnɪst 〕
   - = straightforward
     〔ˌstret'fɔrwəd 〕

5. **strict** 〔 strɪkt 〕 *adj.* 嚴格的
   - = severe 〔 sə'vɪr 〕
   - = firm 〔 fɜm 〕
   - = rigorous 〔 'rɪgərəs 〕

6. **sympathetic** 〔ˌsɪmpə'θɛtɪk 〕
   adj. 同情的
   - = caring 〔 'kɛrɪŋ 〕
   - = kind 〔 kaɪnd 〕
   - = warm 〔 wɔrm 〕
   - = supportive 〔 sə'portɪv 〕

7. **solid** 〔 'sɑlɪd 〕 *adj.* 堅固的；
   可靠的
   - = reliable 〔 rɪ'laɪəbḷ 〕
   - = firm 〔 fɜm 〕
   - = stable 〔'stebḷ 〕

8. **stable** 〔'stebḷ 〕 *adj.* 穩定的
   - = constant 〔 'kɑnstənt 〕
   - = reliable 〔 rɪ'laɪəbḷ 〕
   - = solid 〔'sɑlɪd 〕

9. **straightforward**
   〔ˌstret'fɔrwəd 〕 *adj.* 直率的；
   直接了當的
   - = frank 〔 fræŋk 〕
   - = blunt 〔 blʌnt 〕
   - = honest 〔 'ɑnɪst 〕
   - = direct 〔 də'rɛkt 〕

 **How to Succeed**

21. S (2)

看英文唸出中文	一口氣說九句	看中文唸出英文

strive⁴
〔 straɪv 〕 v.

struggle²
〔'strʌgl̩ 〕 v.

sacrifice⁴
〔'sækrə,faɪs 〕 v. n.

字首都是 S
《
Strive.
要努力。
Struggle.
要奮鬥。
Sacrifice.
要犧牲。
》字首是 Str

努力

掙扎；奮鬥

犧牲

---

surpass⁶
〔 sɚ'pæs 〕 v.

survey³
〔 sɚ've 〕 v.

survive²
〔 sɚ'vaɪv 〕 v.

字首都是 Sur
《
Surpass.
要超越。
Survey.
要做調查。
Survive.
要存活下來。
》字首是 Surv

超越

調查

生還

---

support²
〔 sə'port 〕 v.

supervise⁵
〔'supɚ,vaɪz 〕 v.

succeed²
〔 sək'sid 〕 v.

字首都是 Su
《
Support.
要支持別人。
Supervise.
要監督。
Succeed.
要成功。
》字首是 Sup

支持

監督

成功

I. 背景説明：

　　Strive. (要努力。) *Strive* to do better every time. (每一次都要努力做得更好。) *Strive* for perfection. (要努力追求完美。) *Struggle*. (要奮鬥。) *Struggle* for survival. (要奮鬥求生存。) *Struggle* for the right thing. (要爲對的事情奮鬥。) *Sacrifice*. (要犧牲。) *Sacrifice* your comfort to succeed. (要爲了成功犧牲自己的舒適。) *Sacrifice* yourself for the goal. (要爲了目標犧牲自己。)

　　Surpass. (要超越。) *Surpass* your previous achievements. (要超越你之前的成就。) *Surpass* what you thought was possible. (要超越你以前認爲可能做到的事。) (= *Go beyond what you thought you could do.*) *Survey*. (要做調查。) *Survey* what is around you. (要調查你周圍的事物。) *Survey* your options. (要調查你可選擇的事物。) *Survive*. (要存活下來。) *Survive* every challenge. (經過每次挑戰，都要存活下來。) *Survive* every difficulty. (要從困難中生還。) survive 的意思有：①生還②自…中生還。

　　Support. (要支持別人。) (= *Support others.*) *Support* the project. (要支持所訂的計劃。) *Supervise*. (要監督。) *Supervise* others. (要監督別人。) *Supervise* the situation. (要監督情況。) *Succeed*. (要成功。) *Succeed* in all you do. (做什麼事都要成功。) *Succeed* where others have failed. (別人已經失敗的地方，你要成功。)

II. 英語演講：

【一字英語演講】　　　　【短篇英語演講】

Ladies and gentlemen, *boys and girls:*

Strive.
Struggle.
Sacrifice.

Surpass.
Survey.
Survive.

Support.
Supervise.
Succeed.

Success can be yours!

Ladies and gentlemen, *boys and girls:*
各位先生和女士，男孩和女孩：

Strive to do better every time.
每一次都要努力做得更好。
Struggle for the right thing.　要為對的事情奮鬥。
Sacrifice your comfort to succeed.
要為了成功犧牲自己的舒適。

Surpass what you thought was possible.
要超越你以前認為可能做到的事。
Survey what is around you.　要調查你周圍的事物。
Survive every difficulty.　要從困難中生還。

Support others.　要支持別人。
Supervise the situation.　要監督情況。
Succeed where others have failed.
別人已經失敗的地方，你要成功。

Success can be yours!　成功就會是你的！

III. 短篇作文：

Succeed in Everything

　　To succeed in everything you do, you must *strive* for perfection and *struggle* for survival. *Indeed*, you must *sacrifice* yourself for the goal. *Survey* the situation, *support* the project, and *supervise* others. *Meanwhile*, to *surpass* your previous achievements, you must *survive* every challenge that comes your way. This is how to *succeed*.

每件事都成功

想要做每件事都成功，就必須努力追求完美，而且要奮鬥求生存。的確，你必須爲了目標犧牲自己。要調查情況、支持所訂的計畫，並監督別人。同時，要超越你之前的成就，你必須從你所面臨的每個挑戰中存活下來。這就是成功之道。

* perfection〔pɚˋfɛkʃən〕*n.* 完美
  survival〔səˋvaɪvl̩〕*n.* 生存；生還
  previous〔ˋprivɪəs〕*adj.* 先前的
  come *one's* **way** 發生在某人身上；被某人碰到

IV. 填空：

Successful people ___1___ to do better every time. They ___2___ and fight like crazy to achieve their dreams. They ___3___ their comfort to succeed.

Therefore, you must ___4___ what you thought was possible. ___5___ what is around you. ___6___ every difficulty.

Meanwhile, ___7___ others. ___8___ the situation. ___9___ where others have failed.

成功的人每一次都會努力做得更好。他們會拼命奮鬥達成夢想。他們會爲了成功，犧牲自己的舒適。

因此，你必須超越你以前認爲可能做到的事。要調查你周圍的事物。要從困難中生還。

同時，要支持別人。要監督情況。別人已經失敗的地方，你要成功。

【解答】 1. strive　 2. struggle　 3. sacrifice　 4. surpass
　　　　 5. Survey　 6. Survive　 7. support　 8. Supervise
　　　　 9. Succeed　　 * *like crazy* 拼命地

V. 詞彙題：

Directions: *Choose the one word that best completes the sentence.*

1. You can't improve without _____ to be better.
   (A) sighing   (B) striving   (C) strolling   (D) stinking

2. Be eager and willing to _____ for success.
   (A) struggle   (B) startle   (C) sprinkle   (D) sneeze

3. Nothing good will come unless you're willing to _____.
   (A) stammer   (B) suspect   (C) stumble   (D) sacrifice

4. Don't be happy until you _____ your own expectations.
   (A) surrender   (B) suspend   (C) surpass   (D) sympathize

5. Don't move ahead without _____ the landscape.
   (A) supposing   (B) surrounding   (C) supplying
   (D) surveying

6. Only the strong will _____.
   (A) survive   (B) stutter   (C) shriek   (D) shudder

7. There is nothing more important than _____ a worthy cause.
   (A) shunning   (B) smashing   (C) supporting   (D) skipping

8. Pick the best manager to _____ the team.
   (A) speculate   (B) supervise   (C) summarize   (D) sprain

9. No one can _____ without failure.
   (A) suffer   (B) summon   (C) swear   (D) succeed

【答案】1. (B)   2. (A)   3. (D)   4. (C)   5. (D)   6. (A)
　　　　7. (C)   8. (B)   9. (D)

VI. 同義字整理：

1. **strive** 〔 straɪv 〕 *v.* 努力
   - = try 〔 traɪ 〕
   - = toil 〔 tɔɪl 〕
   - = struggle 〔'strʌgḷ 〕
   - = fight 〔 faɪt 〕

2. **struggle** 〔'strʌgḷ 〕 *v.* 掙扎；
   奮鬥
   - = strive 〔 straɪv 〕
   - = endeavor 〔 ɪn'dɛvɚ 〕
   - = fight 〔 faɪt 〕

3. **sacrifice** 〔'sækrəˌfaɪs 〕 *v. n.*
   犧牲
   - = relinquish 〔 rɪ'lɪŋkwɪʃ 〕
   - = forego 〔 for'go 〕
   - = renounce 〔 rɪ'naʊns 〕

4. **surpass** 〔 sɚ'pæs 〕 *v.* 超越
   - = outdo 〔ˌaʊt'du 〕
   - = beat 〔 bit 〕
   - = excel 〔 ɪk'sɛl 〕

5. **survey** 〔 sɚ've 〕 *v.* 調查
   - = examine 〔 ɪg'zæmɪn 〕
   - = appraise 〔 ə'prez 〕

6. **survive** 〔 sɚ'vaɪv 〕 *v.* 生還；
   存活
   - = persist 〔 pɚ'sɪst 〕
   - = exist 〔 ɪg'zɪst 〕
   - = live on
   - = remain alive

7. **support** 〔 sə'port 〕 *v.* 支持
   - = help 〔 hɛlp 〕
   - = back 〔 bæk 〕
   - = assist 〔 ə'sɪst 〕
   - = side with

8. **supervise** 〔'supɚˌvaɪz 〕 *v.*
   監督
   - = observe 〔 əb'zɝv 〕
   - = guide 〔 gaɪd 〕
   - = monitor 〔'manətɚ 〕
   - = oversee 〔ˌovɚ'si 〕

9. **succeed** 〔 sək'sid 〕 *v.* 成功
   - = thrive 〔 θraɪv 〕
   - = prosper 〔'praspɚ 〕
   - = make it
   - = be successful

How to Succeed

22. T

看英文唸出中文	一口氣說九句	看中文唸出英文
target[2] 〔ˈtɑrgɪt〕*n.*	Have a *target*. 要有目標。 *Train*. 要訓練自己。 *Tolerate*. 要容忍。	目標　 訓練 容忍；忍受

字首都是 t　這兩個是動詞

tidy[3] 〔ˈtaɪdɪ〕*adj.*	Be *tidy*. 要整潔。 *Thirsty*. 要渴望成功。 *Thrifty*. 要節儉。	整齊的　 口渴的；渴望的 節儉的
thirsty[2] 〔ˈθɝstɪ〕*adj.*		
thrifty[6] 〔ˈθrɪftɪ〕*adj.*		

字首都是 t　是 ty 結尾的形容詞

tactful[6] 〔ˈtæktfəl〕*adj.*	*Tactful*. 說話要婉轉。 *Thankful*. 要心存感激。 *Thoughtful*. 要體貼。	圓滑的 感激的 體貼的
thankful[3] 〔ˈθæŋkfəl〕*adj.*		
thoughtful[4] 〔ˈθɔtfəl〕*adj.*		

字首是 Th　字尾都是 ful

I. 背景説明：

Have a target.（要有目標。）(= *Have a goal.*) Set a *target.*（要設定目標。）See the *target.*（要看到目標。）*Train.*（要訓練自己。）(= *Train yourself.*) *Train* your mind to work hard.（要訓練自己的心態去努力工作。）*Tolerate.*（要容忍。）*Tolerate* changes.（要容忍改變。）*Tolerate* others.（要容忍他人。）

Be tidy.（要整潔。）Keep a *tidy* desk.（辦公桌要保持整潔。）*Thirsty.*（要很渴望。）(= *Be thirsty.*) Be *thirsty* for success.（要渴望成功。）Be *thirsty* for knowledge.（要渴望獲得知識。）*Thrifty.*（要節儉。）(= *Be thrifty.*) Be a *thrifty* worker.（要當一個節儉的員工。）Be *thrifty* with money.（要節省用錢。）ty 是名詞字尾，但 thirsty、thrifty 和 guilty（有罪的）例外。(詳見「文法寶典」p.72)

Tactful.（說話要婉轉。）(= *Be tactful. = Be a tactful speaker. = Speak tactfully.*) *Thankful.*（要心存感激。）(= *Be thankful.*) Be *thankful* for everything.（要對任何事都心存感激。）Be *thankful* for every opportunity.（要對每個機會都心存感激。）*Thoughtful.*（要體貼。）(= *Be thoughtful.*) Be a *thoughtful* friend.（要做一個體貼的朋友。）Have a *thoughtful* outlook.（看法要體貼。）

II. 英語演講：

【一字英語演講】	【短篇英語演講】
Ladies and gentlemen:	*Ladies and gentlemen:* 各位先生，各位女士：
Have a target. *Train.* *Tolerate.*	*Have a target.* 要有目標。 *Train* yourself. 要訓練自己。 *Tolerate* changes. 要容忍改變。
Be tidy. *Thirsty.* *Thrifty.*	*Be* a *tidy* person. 要做一個整潔的人。 Be *thirsty* for knowledge. 要渴望獲得知識。 Be a *thrifty* worker. 要當一個節儉的員工。
Tactful. *Thankful.* *Thoughtful.*	Be a *tactful* speaker. 說話要婉轉。 Be *thankful* for every opportunity. 要對每個機會都心存感激。 Be a *thoughtful* friend. 要做一個體貼的朋友。
You will achieve success!	*You will achieve success!* 你一定會成功！

III. 短篇作文：

The Way to Success

　　Successful people have many things in common. *First*, they see a *target* and go for it. They don't *tolerate* failure. They are very *tidy*. *Second*, successful people *train* themselves to work hard. They are *thirsty* for knowledge and *thrifty* with money. *What's more*, successful people are *tactful*; they think before they speak. *Above all*, successful people are *thoughtful* friends and *thankful* for everything they have.

成功之道

　　成功的人有很多共同點。首先，他們會看到目標，並全力以赴。他們不會容忍失敗。他們非常整潔。第二，成功的人會訓練自己努力工作。他們渴望獲得知識，並且節省用錢。此外，成功的人說話很婉轉；他們都會先想好再說。最重要的是，成功的人是體貼的朋友，並對他們所擁有的一切心存感激。

IV. 填空：

　　To succeed, you must choose a ___1___ and stay focused on achieving the goal. ___2___ yourself as if you were preparing for battle. Never ___3___ failure.

　　On top of that, be a ___4___ and organized person. Be ___5___ for knowledge. Be a ___6___ and efficient worker.

　　Being ___7___ is beneficial to communication. Likewise, it doesn't cost anything to be polite. It will save you a lot of trouble. People who are ___8___ for what they have are usually ___9___ as well.

　　要成功，你必須選擇一個目標，並專注於達成這個目標。要像是準備要戰鬥一樣地訓練自己。絕不能容忍失敗。

　　此外，要做個整潔而且有條理的人。要渴望獲得知識。要當一個節儉而且有效率的員工。

　　說話婉轉對溝通有益。同樣地，禮貌不花一毛錢。它能讓你省去很多麻煩。對所擁有的一切心存感激的人，通常也會很體貼。

【解答】　1. target　　2. Train　　3. tolerate　　4. tidy　　5. thirsty
　　　　　6. thrifty　　7. tactful　　8. thankful　　9. thoughtful

　　　* organized (ˈɔrgənˌaɪzd) *adj.* 有條理的
　　　　beneficial (ˌbɛnəˈfɪʃəl) *adj.* 有益的
　　　on top of that 此外　　***as well*** 也 (= *too*)

V. 詞彙題：

Directions: *Choose the one word that best completes the sentence.*

1. Set a _____ and go for it without delay.
   (A) target　(B) tradition　(C) theory　(D) thriller

2. Successful people _____ themselves to work hard.
   (A) trap　(B) train　(C) tread　(D) twist

3. Learn how to _____ difficulties.
   (A) translate　(B) tangle　(C) terrify　(D) tolerate

4. Maintain a _____ workspace.
   (A) tiresome　(B) tiny　(C) tidy　(D) timid

5. Be _____ for knowledge and experience.
   (A) thorough　(B) thirsty　(C) tough　(D) tolerable

6. You must be _____ with both time and money.
   (A) typical　(B) tricky　(C) tasty　(D) thrifty

7. Social and business relationships require a _____ manner.
   (A) tactful　(B) talkative　(C) temporary　(D) tentative

8. Be _____ for every opportunity that comes your way.
   (A) transparent　(B) theoretical　(C) traditional
   (D) thankful

9. A _____ person is considerate and kind.
   (A) trivial　(B) triumphant　(C) thoughtful　(D) tragic

【答案】1.（A）　2.（B）　3.（D）　4.（C）　5.（B）　6.（D）
　　　　7.（A）　8.（D）　9.（C）

VI. 同義字整理：

1. **target** (ˈtɑrgɪt) *n.* 目標
   = goal (gol)
   = aim (em)
   = objective (əbˈdʒɛktɪv)

2. **train** (tren) *v.* 訓練
   = practice (ˈpræktɪs)
   = prepare (prɪˈpɛr)
   = make ready

3. **tolerate** (ˈtɑlə͵ret) *v.* 容忍
   = endure (ɪnˈdjur)
   = suffer (ˈsʌfə)
   = bear (bɛr)
   = take (tek)

4. **tidy** (ˈtaɪdɪ) *adj.* 整齊的
   = neat (nit)
   = organized (ˈɔrgən͵aɪzd)
   = clean (klin)

5. **thirsty** (ˈθɝstɪ) *adj.* 口渴的；
   渴望的
   = hungry (ˈhʌŋgrɪ)
   = wishful (ˈwɪʃfəl)

6. **thrifty** (ˈθrɪftɪ) *adj.* 節儉的
   = economical (͵ikəˈnɑmɪkl̩)
   = frugal (ˈfrugl̩)
   = prudent (ˈprudn̩t)

7. **tactful** (ˈtæktfəl) *adj.* 圓滑的
   = diplomatic (͵dɪpləˈmætɪk)
   = polite (pəˈlaɪt)
   = polished (ˈpɑlɪʃt)

8. **thankful** (ˈθæŋkfəl) *adj.*
   感激的
   = grateful (ˈgretfəl)
   = obliged (əˈblaɪdʒd)
   = appreciative
     (əˈpriʃɪ͵etɪv)

9. **thoughtful** (ˈθɔtfəl) *adj.*
   體貼的
   = considerate (kənˈsɪdərɪt)
   = reflective (rɪˈflɛktɪv)
   = attentive (əˈtɛntɪv)

How to Succeed

23. V

看英文唸出中文	一口氣説九句	看中文唸出英文
venture[5] 〔ˈvɛntʃə〕 *v.*	三個都是動詞 ⎱ ***Venture.*** 要勇於冒險。	冒險
visualize[6] 〔ˈvɪʒuəlˌaɪz〕 *v.*	***Visualize.*** 要會想像。	想像
volunteer[4] 〔ˌvɑlənˈtɪr〕 *v.*	***Volunteer.*** 要自願幫忙。	自願

---

valuable[3] 〔ˈvæljuəbl̩〕 *adj.*	字首是 va ⎱ Be ***valuable.*** 要有價值。 ⎰ 字尾是 able	有價值的
variable[6] 〔ˈvɛrɪəbl̩ , ˈvæ-〕 *adj.*	***Variable.*** 要懂得變通。	多變的；可變的
valiant[6] 〔ˈvæljənt〕 *adj.*	***Valiant.*** 要勇敢果決。	英勇的

---

vital[4] 〔ˈvaɪtl̩〕 *adj.*	字首是 Vi ⎱ ***Vital.*** 要充滿活力。 ⎰ 字尾都唸 /tl̩/	非常重要的； 充滿活力的
versatile[6] 〔ˈvɜsətl̩ ,-taɪl〕 *adj.*	***Versatile.*** 要多才多藝。	多才多藝的
vigorous[5] 〔ˈvɪgərəs〕 *adj.*	***Vigorous.*** 要精力充沛。	精力充沛的

I. 背景説明：

Venture.（要勇於冒險。）英文有句諺語：Nothing *ventured*, nothing gained.（不冒險將一無所得。）要成功，就要有冒險的精神。*Venture* to start your own business.（要冒險創業。）*Visualize*.（要會想像。）*Visualize* your dreams.（要想像你的夢想。）*Visualize* your goal.（要想像你的目標。）*Volunteer*.（要自願幫忙。）（= *Be a volunteer*.）*Volunteer* your time.（要自願付出你的時間。）*Volunteer* to do tough tasks.（要自願做困難的工作。）

Be valuable.（要有價值。）Be invaluable.（要很珍貴。）Be valued.（要受重視。）Be a *valuable* team member.（要做一個有價值的團隊成員。）*Variable*.（要懂得變通。）（= *Be variable*. = *Be flexible and changeable*.）Be *variable* and helpful.（要懂得變通而且樂於助人。）Have a *variable* mind.（想法要懂得變通。）*Valiant*.（要勇敢果決。）（= *Be valiant*. = *Be very brave and determined*.）Be *valiant* and loyal.（要英勇而且忠誠。）Be *valiant* and honorable.（要英勇而且令人敬佩。）

Vital.（要充滿活力。）（= *Be vital*.）可加強語氣説成：Be *vital* and strong.（要充滿活力而且強壯。）Have a *vital* personality.（個性要充滿活力。）vital 也可作「非常重要的」解，如：Your attendance is *vital*.（你的出席是非常重要的。）*Versatile*.（要多才多藝。）（= *Be versatile*.）Be a *versatile* professional.（要做個什麼都會的專業人士。）Be *versatile* and dynamic.（要多才多藝而且充滿活力。）*Vigorous*.（要精力充沛。）（= *Be vigorous*.）可加長爲：Be *vigorous* and persistent.（要精力充沛而且不屈不撓。）

II. 英語演講：

| 【一字英語演講】 | 【短篇英語演講】 |

To all those in attendance:

Venture.
Visualize.
Volunteer.

Be valuable
Variable.
Valiant.

Vital.
Versatile.
Vigorous.

Success is your destiny.

To all those in attendance: 各位出席的來賓：

Nothing *ventured*, nothing gained.
不冒險將一無所得。
Visualize your dreams. 要想像你的夢想。
Volunteer your time. 要自願付出你的時間。

Be a *valuable* team member.
要做一個有價值的團隊成員。
Be *variable* and helpful. 要懂得變通又樂於助人。
Be *valiant* and brave. 要非常勇敢。

Have a *vital* personality. 個性要充滿活力。
Be *versatile* and dynamic.
要多才多藝而且充滿活力。
Be *vigorous* and persistent.
要精力充沛而且不屈不撓。

Success is your destiny. 你終將成功。

III. 短篇作文：

The Keys to Success

Here are the keys to success. *Venture* to start your own business. *Visualize* your dreams. *Volunteer* your time. *Be* a *valuable* team member. Be *variable* and helpful. *What's more*, be *valiant* and brave. Have a *vital* personality. Be *versatile* and dynamic. Be *vigorous* and persistent. You will achieve success.

成功的祕訣

以下是成功的秘訣。要冒險創業。要想像你的夢想。要自願付出你的時間。要做一個有價值的團隊成員。要懂得變通,而且樂於助人。此外,要非常勇敢。個性要充滿活力。要多才多藝而且充滿活力。要精力充沛而且不屈不撓。你一定會成功。

IV. 填空:

Achieving success isn't easy, but as they say, nothing ___1___, nothing gained. ___2___ your dreams coming true. Be happy to ___3___ for difficult tasks.

At the same time, be a ___4___ worker by always putting the team first. Be ___5___ and helpful. Be ___6___ and brave enough to accept challenges.

In fact, a successful person has a ___7___ personality. Be a ___8___ and dynamic employee, capable of many different things. Be ___9___ and persistent, never willing to give up.

成功並不容易,但正如俗話所說的,不冒險將一無所得。要想像你的夢想成真。要樂於自願做困難的工作。

同時,要做一個有價值的員工,總是把團隊放在第一位。要懂得變通而且樂於助人。要夠勇敢,願意接受挑戰。

事實上,成功的人會有充滿活力的個性。要做一個多才多藝而且充滿活力的員工,能夠做很多不同的事。要精力充沛而且不屈不撓,絕不願放棄。

【解答】 1. ventured　2. Visualize　3. volunteer　4. valuable
　　　　 5. variable 6. valiant 7. vital 8. versatile 9. vigorous
　　　　　* *as they say* 正如大家所說
　　　　　 dynamic〔daɪˈnæmɪk〕*adj.* 充滿活力的
　　　　　 persistent〔pəˈsɪstənt〕*adj.* 不屈不撓的

V. 詞彙題：

Directions: *Choose the one word that best completes the sentence.*

1. Don't be afraid to ＿＿＿＿ into unknown territory.
   (A) vow　(B) vote　(C) vacuum　(D) venture

2. ＿＿＿＿ your success as you would like to see it happen.
   (A) Visualize　(B) Victimize　(C) Violate　(D) Vibrate

3. You're never too busy to ＿＿＿＿ to help.
   (A) volunteer　(B) vary　(C) vomit　(D) vanish

4. Every experience, whether positive or negative, is ＿＿＿＿.
   (A) vacant　(B) various　(C) valuable　(D) vicious

5. Set ＿＿＿＿ goals, depending on the situation.
   (A) verbal　(B) variable　(C) volcanic　(D) vocal

6. Your success will require a ＿＿＿＿ effort.
   (A) vivid　(B) valiant　(C) vain　(D) vague

7. Be ＿＿＿＿, dynamic, and energetic.
   (A) vocational　(B) vulgar　(C) vital　(D) virtual

8. Be ＿＿＿＿ and capable of many things.
   (A) versatile　(B) violent　(C) verbal　(D) vulnerable

9. Be a ＿＿＿＿ and robust person.
   (A) vertical　(B) visible　(C) various　(D) vigorous

【答案】1.（D）　2.（A）　3.（A）　4.（C）　5.（B）　6.（B）
　　　　7.（C）　8.（A）　9.（D）

VI. 同義字整理：

1. **venture**〔ˋvɛntʃə〕 *v.* 冒險
   - = have the courage to
   - = dare〔dɛr〕
   - = hazard〔ˋhæzəd〕

2. **visualize**〔ˋvɪʒʊəl‚aɪz〕 *v.* 想像
   - = picture〔ˋpɪktʃə〕
   - = imagine〔ɪˋmædʒɪn〕
   - = conceive〔kənˋsiv〕

3. **volunteer**〔‚vɑlənˋtɪr〕 *v.* 自願
   - = offer〔ˋɔfə〕
   - = propose〔prəˋpoz〕

4. **valuable**〔ˋvæljʊəbḷ〕 *adj.*
   有價值的
   - = precious〔ˋprɛʃəs〕
   - = priceless〔ˋpraɪslɪs〕
   - = invaluable〔ɪnˋvæljəbḷ〕

5. **variable**〔ˋvɛrɪəbḷ‚ˋvæ-〕 *adj.*
   多變的；可變的
   - = changeable〔ˋtʃendʒəbḷ〕
   - = flexible〔ˋflɛksəbḷ〕

6. **valiant**〔ˋvæljənt〕 *adj.*
   英勇的
   - = brave〔brev〕
   - = bold〔bold〕
   - = courageous〔kəˋredʒəs〕

7. **vital**〔ˋvaɪtḷ〕 *adj.* 非常重
   要的；充滿活力的
   - = lively〔ˋlaɪvlɪ〕
   - = vigorous〔ˋvɪgərəs〕
   - = dynamic〔daɪˋnæmɪk〕

8. **versatile**〔ˋvɝsətḷ‚-taɪl〕 *adj.*
   多才多藝的
   - = flexible〔ˋflɛksəbḷ〕
   - = adaptable〔əˋdæptəbḷ〕
   - = resourceful〔rɪˋsorsfəl〕

9. **vigorous**〔ˋvɪgərəs〕 *adj.*
   精力充沛的
   - = energetic〔‚ɛnəˋdʒɛtɪk〕
   - = robust〔roˋbʌst〕
   - = vital〔ˋvaɪtḷ〕

How to Succeed

24. W

看英文唸出中文	一口氣說九句	看中文唸出英文
warm[1] 〔 wɔrm 〕 *adj.*	字首是wa {	Be *warm*. 要熱心。	溫暖的；熱心的
wary[5] 〔'wɛrɪ 〕 *adj.*		*Wary*. 要謹慎。	小心的；謹慎的
wise[2] 〔 waɪz 〕 *adj.*		*Wise*. 要聰明。	聰明的

worthy[5] 〔'wɜðɪ 〕 *adj.*	都有Worth {	*Worthy*. 要有價值。	值得的
worthwhile[5] 〔'wɜθ'hwaɪl 〕 *adj.*		*Worthwhile*. 要有用。	值得的；有用的
wholesome[5] 〔'holsəm 〕 *adj.*		*Wholesome*. 要健康。	有益健康的； 健康的

willing[2] 〔'wɪlɪŋ 〕 *adj.*	字首都是wi {	*Willing*. 要願意嘗試。	願意的
witty[6] 〔'wɪtɪ 〕 *adj.*		*Witty*. 說話要風趣。	說話風趣的
winner[2] 〔'wɪnɚ 〕 *n.*		A *winner*. 要成為贏家。	優勝者

I. 背景説明：

Be warm.（要熱心。）可説成：Have a *warm* smile.（要有親切的微笑。）Be *warm* and welcoming.（要熱心而且好客。）warm 的意思有「溫暖的；熱心的；親切的」。*Wary*.（要謹慎。）(= *Be wary*.) Be *wary* of danger.（要小心危險。）Be *wary* of risk.（要小心風險。）*Wise*.（要聰明。）(= *Be wise*.) Make *wise* decisions.（要做聰明的決定。）Be a *wise* investor.（要做個聰明的投資者。）

Worthy.（要有價值。）(= *Be worthy*. = *Be valuable*.) Be *worthy* of your salary.（要對得起你的薪水。）Be *worthy* of your position.（要配得上你的職位。）*Worthwhile*.（要有用。）(= *Be worthwhile*. = *Be useful*.) Do *worthwhile* things.（要做有價值的事。）Spend your time on *worthwhile* projects.（要把時間花在有價值的計劃上。）*Wholesome*.（要健康。）(= *Be wholesome*.)可加長爲：Have a *wholesome* attitude.（要有健康的心態。）Be *wholesome* and trustworthy.（要健康而且值得信任。）wholesome 的意思有「有益健康的」和「健康的」。

Willing.（要願意嘗試。）(= *Be willing*.) Be *willing* to try anything.（要願意嘗試任何事。）Be *willing* to sacrifice.（要願意犧牲。）Be *willing* to go the extra mile.（要願意特別努力。）*Witty*.（說話要風趣。）(= *Be witty*. = *Be clever and funny*.)可加長爲：Be *witty* in conversation.（和別人談話要風趣。）Be *witty* and charming.（要風趣又有魅力。）witty 在英式英語中，也作「機智的」解。*A winner*.（要成爲贏家。）(= *Be a winner*.)可説成：*A winner* never complains.（贏家永遠不會抱怨。）Work hard and be a *winner*.（努力工作就能成爲贏家。）

II. 英語演講：

<table>
<tr><td>

【一字英語演講】

</td><td>

【短篇英語演講】

</td></tr>
<tr><td>

Students, parents, teachers, friends:

</td><td>

Students, parents, teachers, friends:
各位同學、家長、老師、朋友們：

</td></tr>
<tr><td>

Be warm.
Wary.
Wise.

</td><td>

Be warm. 要熱心。
Be *wary* of danger. 要小心危險。
Make *wise* decisions. 要做聰明的決定。

</td></tr>
<tr><td>

Worthy.
Worthwhile.
Wholesome.

</td><td>

Be *worthy* of your position. 要配得上你的職位。
Do *worthwhile* things. 要做有價值的事。
Have a *wholesome* attitude. 要有健康的心態。

</td></tr>
<tr><td>

Willing.
Witty.
A winner.

</td><td>

Be *willing* to try anything. 要願意嘗試任何事。
Be *witty* and charming. 要風趣又有魅力。
Work hard and be *a winner*.
努力工作就能成為贏家。

</td></tr>
<tr><td>

This is how you will succeed.

</td><td>

This is how you will succeed.
這就是你成功的方法。

</td></tr>
</table>

III. 短篇作文：

The Secret of Success

Success means being the best you can be. But what are some of those things to "be"? Here are nine things to be if you want to achieve success: *Be warm*. Be *wary* of risk. Be *wise*. Be *worthy* of praise. Be a *worthwhile* asset. Be a *wholesome* person. Be *willing* to go the extra mile. Be *witty* in conversation. *And most of all*, be *a winner*.

成功的祕訣

成功就意謂著盡力做到最好。但必須「做好」的事情包括哪些？如果你想成功，以下有九件事情是你必須做好的：要熱心。要小心風險。要聰明。要值得受到稱讚。要成爲有用的資產。要做個健康的人。要願意特別努力。說話要風趣。而且最重要的是，要成爲贏家。

IV. 填空：

Many successful people have a ___1___ smile that makes people feel good. They're ___2___ of problems that might occur. They make ___3___ decisions.

To be honest, you have to work very hard to be ___4___ of praise. However, if you do ___5___ things and have a ___6___ attitude, recognition is certain to come.

Therefore, you must be ___7___ to try anything. Be ___8___ and charming. Most of all, work hard and be a ___9___.

很多成功的人都有親切的微笑，讓大家感覺很好。他們會小心可能發生的問題。他們會做聰明的決定。

老實說，你必須非常努力，才值得被稱讚。然而，如果你做了有價值的事，並且有健康的心態，一定會被認可。

因此，你就必須願意嘗試任何事。要風趣又有魅力。最重要的是，努力工作就能成爲贏家。

【解答】 1. warm　2. wary　3. wise　4. worthy　5. worthwhile
　　　　6. wholesome　7. willing　8. witty　9. winner

to be honest 老實說
recognition〔͵rɛkəgˋnɪʃən〕*n.* 承認；認可
most of all 最重要的是

V. 詞彙題：

Directions: *Choose the one word that best completes the sentence.*

1. Everybody loves a ＿＿＿＿ and friendly smile.
   (A) wrong　(B) whirling　(C) weighty　(D) warm

2. Keep a ＿＿＿＿ eye out for trouble ahead.
   (A) wary　(B) wishful　(C) willing　(D) wonderful

3. The ＿＿＿＿ person makes good decisions.
   (A) worst　(B) woolen　(C) wise　(D) wireless

4. There's a peace of mind in being ＿＿＿＿ of your position.
   (A) weary　(B) worthy　(C) wealthy　(D) weak

5. Successful people do ＿＿＿＿ things.
   (A) weekly　(B) western　(C) worthwhile　(D) waterproof

6. Make a favorable impression with your ＿＿＿＿ attitude.
   (A) wholesome　(B) wholesale　(C) whole　(D) weird

7. If you're ＿＿＿＿ to try anything, success can be yours.
   (A) wicked　(B) widespread　(C) wild　(D) willing

8. People will admire your ＿＿＿＿ conversation.
   (A) wooden　(B) windy　(C) witty　(D) wide

9. Work hard and be a ＿＿＿＿ at anything you do.
   (A) wrinkle　(B) winner　(C) wreath　(D) witness

【答案】 1. (D)　2. (A)　3. (C)　4. (B)　5. (C)　6. (A)
　　　　 7. (D)　8. (C)　9. (B)

VI. 同義字整理：

1. **warm** 〔 wɔrm 〕 *adj.* 溫暖的；
   熱心的；親切的
   - = affectionate 〔 əˋfɛkʃənɪt 〕
   - = friendly 〔ˋfrɛndlɪ 〕
   - = hospitable 〔ˋhɑspɪtəbḷ 〕

2. **wary** 〔ˋwɛrɪ 〕 *adj.* 小心的；
   謹慎的
   - = cautious 〔ˋkɔʃəs 〕
   - = watchful 〔ˋwɑtʃfəl 〕
   - = alert 〔 əˋlɜt 〕

3. **wise** 〔 waɪz 〕 *adj.* 聰明的
   - = clever 〔ˋklɛvɚ 〕
   - = intelligent 〔 ɪnˋtɛlədʒənt 〕
   - = sensible 〔ˋsɛnsəbḷ 〕

4. **worthy** 〔ˋwɜðɪ 〕 *adj.* 值得的
   - = valuable 〔ˋvæljuəbḷ 〕
   - = worthwhile 〔ˋwɜθˋhwaɪl 〕
   - = honorable 〔ˋɑnərəbḷ 〕
   - = respectable 〔 rɪˋspɛktəbḷ 〕

5. **worthwhile** 〔ˋwɜθˋhwaɪl 〕
   adj. 值得的；有用的
   - = valuable 〔ˋvæljuəbḷ 〕
   - = helpful 〔ˋhɛlpfəl 〕
   - = worthy 〔ˋwɜðɪ 〕

6. **wholesome** 〔ˋholsəm 〕
   adj. 有益健康的；健康的
   - = healthy 〔ˋhɛlθɪ 〕
   - = good 〔 gʊd 〕

7. **willing** 〔ˋwɪlɪŋ 〕 *adj.* 願意的
   - = inclined 〔 ɪnˋklaɪnd 〕
   - = prepared 〔 prɪˋpɛrd 〕
   - = pleased 〔 plizd 〕

8. **witty** 〔ˋwɪtɪ 〕 *adj.* 說話風趣的
   - = clever 〔ˋklɛvɚ 〕
   - = humorous 〔ˋhjumərəs 〕
   - = brilliant 〔ˋbrɪljənt 〕

9. **winner** 〔ˋwɪnɚ 〕 *n.* 優勝者
   - = victor 〔ˋvɪktɚ 〕
   - = champion 〔ˋtʃæmpɪən 〕
   - = conqueror 〔ˋkɑŋkərɚ 〕

INDEX・索引

※ 可利用索引，檢查你是否都認識這些字。

How to Succeed

全書 216 句

聽「英文一字金」就和聽唸經一樣，再重複不停地唸，就能脫口而出！

1. Attend.
   Adjust.
   Adapt.

   一回九句，
   可用手機重
   複循環聽。

   Achieve.
   Accomplish.
   Accumulate.

   Be active.
   Acute.
   Aggressive.

4. Control.
   Concentrate.
   Cultivate.

   Cooperate.
   Coordinate.
   Create.

   Communicate.
   Complete.
   Commit yourself.

2. Bear.
   Bloom.
   Be blunt.

   Beware.
   Benefit.
   Believe in yourself.

   Break through.
   Be brilliant.
   Broaden your horizons.

5. Desire.
   Demand.
   Determine.

   Devote.
   Develop.
   Discover.

   Discuss.
   Defeat fear.
   Dedicate yourself.

3. Chase.
   Cheer.
   Cherish.

   Conquer.
   Confront.
   Contribute.

   Be confident.
   Competent.
   Competitive.

6. Decide.
   Devise.
   Dominate.

   Dare.
   Dazzle.
   Differentiate.

   Differ.
   Dispose.
   Diversify.

7. Express.
   Explore.
   Be eloquent.

   Encourage.
   Endeavor.
   Evolve.

   Excel.
   Execute.
   Be excellent.

10. Be helpful.
    Hopeful.
    Humorous.

    Humble.
    Honorable.
    Hospitable.

    Hardy.
    Hearty.
    Healthy.

8. Follow.
   Focus.
   Found.

   Forgive.
   Fortify.
   Forecast.

   Face.
   Be firm.
   Be flexible.

11. Improve.
    Impress.
    Implement.

    Invent.
    Initiate.
    Innovate.

    Invest.
    Inspire.
    Instruct.

9. Grow.
   Grope.
   Glow.

   Grab.
   Grasp.
   Guide.

   Generate.
   Be generous.
   Be grateful.

12. Have insight.
    Information.
    Imagination.

    Integrity.
    Ingenuity.
    Intelligence.

    Be invaluable.
    Indispensable.
    Impressive.

13. Join.
    Judge.
    Be just.

    Be keen.
    Keep learning.
    Have knowledge.

    Lead.
    Listen.
    Be loyal.

16. Obey.
    Follow orders.
    Seek opportunities.

    Offer.
    Overcome.
    Be obliging.

    Outright.
    Optimistic.
    Outstanding.

14. Measure.
    Manage.
    Maintain.

    Move.
    Motivate.
    Be moral.

    Modify.
    Be modest.
    Encourage mutual efforts.

17. Plan.
    Prepare.
    Produce.

    Persist.
    Persevere.
    Perceive.

    Participate.
    Be positive.
    Be patient.

15. Master.
    Mobilize.
    Modernize.

    Nourish.
    Nurture.
    Negotiate.

    Be neat.
    Normal.
    Noticeable.

18. Respect.
    Remain.
    Resolve.

    Reform.
    Regard.
    Reinforce.

    Require.
    Request.
    Realize your dream.

19. React.
Relax.
Revive.

Refine.
Renew.
Rejoice.

Be rapid.
Radiant.
Robust.

22. Have a target.
Train.
Tolerate.

Be tidy.
Thirsty.
Thrifty.

Tactful.
Thankful.
Thoughtful.

20. Be smart.
Skilled.
Sophisticated.

Sincere.
Strict.
Sympathetic.

Solid.
Stable.
Straightforward.

23. Venture.
Visualize.
Volunteer.

Be valuable.
Variable.
Valiant.

Vital.
Versatile.
Vigorous.

21. Strive.
Struggle.
Sacrifice.

Surpass.
Survey.
Survive.

Support.
Supervise.
Succeed.

24. Be warm.
Wary.
Wise.

Worthy.
Worthwhile.
Wholesome.

Willing.
Witty.
A winner.

本書所有人

姓名 ＿＿＿＿＿＿＿＿＿＿＿＿＿＿＿＿　電話 ＿＿＿＿＿＿＿＿＿＿＿＿

地址 ＿＿＿＿＿＿＿＿＿＿＿＿＿＿＿＿＿＿＿＿＿＿＿＿＿＿＿＿＿＿＿

（如拾獲本書，請通知本人領取，感激不盡。）

「英文一字金①成功勵志經」背誦記錄表

篇　名	口試通過 日　期	口試老師 簽　名	篇　名	口試通過 日　期	口試老師 簽　名
1. A			*13.* J,K,L		
2. B			*14.* M (1)		
3. C (1)			*15.* M (2)		
4. C (2)			*16.* O		
5. D (1)			*17.* P		
6. D (2)			*18.* R (1)		
7. E			*19.* R (2)		
8. F			*20.* S (1)		
9. G			*21.* S (2)		
10. H			*22.* T		
11. I (1)			*23.* V		
12. I (2)			*24.* W		

「財團法人臺北市一口氣英語教育基金會」
提供 *100* 萬元獎金，領完為止！

1. 每一回九句，5 秒鐘內背完。
2. 每次可背多回，每天口試只限 2 次。
3. 在 1 分半鐘內，背完整本 216 句，可得獎金 2,000 元。
4. 5 分鐘內一次背完「英文一字金①～④」，可再得獎金 2,000 元。
5. 背誦地點：台北市許昌街 17 號 6F–6【一口氣英語教育基金會】
　　TEL: (02) 2389-5212

高三同學要如何準備「升大學考試」

　　考前該如何準備「學測」呢？「劉毅英文」的同學很簡單，只要熟讀每次的模考試題就行了。每一份試題都在7000字範圍內，就不必再背7000字了，從後面往前複習，越後面越重要，一定要把最後10份試題唸得滾瓜爛熟。根據以往的經驗，詞彙題絕對不會超出7000字範圍。每年題型變化不大，只要針對下面幾個大題準備即可。

準備「詞彙題」最佳資料：

背了再背，背到滾瓜爛熟，讓背單字變成樂趣。

考前不斷地做模擬試題就對了！

你做的題目愈多，分數就愈高。不要忘記，每次參加模考前，都要背單字、背自己所喜歡的作文。考壞不難過，勇往直前，必可得高分！

練習「模擬試題」，可參考「學習出版公司」最新出版的「7000字學測試題詳解」。我們試題的特色是：

①以「高中常用7000字」為範圍。②經過外籍專家多次校對，不會學錯。③每份試題都有詳細解答，對錯答案均有明確交待。

「克漏字」如何答題

　　第二大題綜合測驗（即「克漏字」），不是考句意，就是考簡單的文法。當四個選項都不相同時，就是考句意，就沒有文法的問題；當四個選項單字相同、字群排列不同時，就是考文法，此時就要注意到文法的分析，大多是考連接詞、分詞構句、時態等。「克漏字」是考生最弱的一環，你難，別人也難，只要考前利用這種答題技巧，勤加練習，就容易勝過別人。

準備「綜合測驗」（克漏字）可參考「學習出版公司」最新出版的「7000字克漏字詳解」。

本書特色：

1. 取材自大規模考試，英雄所見略同。
2. 不超出7000字範圍，不會做白工。
3. 每個句子都有文法分析。一目了然。
4. 對錯答案都有明確交待，列出生字，不用查字典。
5. 經過「劉毅英文」同學實際考過，效果極佳。

「文意選填」答題技巧

　　在做「文意選填」的時候，一定要冷靜。你要記住，一個空格一個答案，如果你不知道該選哪個才好，不妨先把詞性正確的選項挑出來，如介詞後面一定是名詞，選項裡面只有兩個名詞，再用刪去法，把不可能的選項刪掉。也要特別注意時間的掌控，已經用過的選項就劃掉，以免重複考慮，浪費時間。

準備「文意選填」，可參考「學習出版公司」最新出版的「7000字文意選填詳解」。

特色與「7000字克漏字詳解」相同，不超出7000字的範圍，有詳細解答。

「閱讀測驗」的答題祕訣

① 尋找關鍵字──整篇文章中,最重要就是第一句和最後一句,第一句稱為主題句,最後一句稱為結尾句。每段的第一句和最後一句,第二重要,是該段落的主題句和結尾句。從「主題句」和「結尾句」中,找出相同的關鍵字,就是文章的重點。因為美國人從小被訓練,寫作文要注重主題句,他們給學生一個題目後,要求主題句和結尾句都必須有關鍵字。

② 先看題目、劃線、找出答案、標題號──考試的時候,先把閱讀測驗題目瀏覽一遍,在文章中掃瞄和題幹中相同的關鍵字,把和題目相關的句子,用線畫起來,便可一目了然。通常一句話只會考一題,你畫了線以後,再標上題號,接下來,你找其他題目的答案,就會更快了。

③ 碰到難的單字不要害怕,往往在文章的其他地方,會出現同義字,因為寫文章的人不喜歡重覆,所以才會有難的單字。

④ 如果閱測內容已經知道,像時事等,你就可以直接做答了。

準備「閱讀測驗」,可參考「學習出版公司」最新出版的「7000字閱讀測驗詳解」,本書不超出7000字範圍,每個句子都有文法分析,對錯答案都有明確交待,單字註明級數,不需要再查字典。

「中翻英」如何準備

可參考劉毅老師的「英文翻譯句型講座實況DVD」,以及「文法句型180」和「翻譯句型800」。考前不停地練習中翻英,翻完之後,要給外籍老師改。翻譯題做得越多,越熟練。

「英文作文」怎樣寫才能得高分？

① 字體要寫整齊，最好是印刷體，工工整整，不要塗改。

② 文章不可離題，尤其是每段的第一句和最後一句，最好要有題目所說的關鍵字。

③ 不要全部用簡單句，句子最好要有各種變化，單句、複句、合句、形容詞片語、分詞構句等，混合使用。

④ 不要忘記多使用轉承語，像 *at present*（現在），*generally speaking*（一般說來），*in other words*（換句話說），*in particular*（特別地），*all in all*（總而言之）等。

⑤ 拿到考題，最好先寫作文，很多同學考試時，作文來不及寫，吃虧很大。但是，如果看到作文題目不會寫，就先寫測驗題，這個時候，可將題目中作文可使用的單字、成語圈起來，寫作文時就有東西寫了。但千萬記住，絕對不可以抄考卷中的句子，一旦被發現，就會以零分計算。

⑥ 試卷有規定標題，就要寫標題。記住，每段一開始，要內縮5或7個字母。

⑦ 可多引用諺語或名言，並注意標點符號的使用。文章中有各種標點符號，會使文章變得更美。

⑧ 整體的美觀也很重要，段落的最後一行字數不能太少，也不能太多。段落的字數要平均分配，不能第一段只有一、兩句，第二段一大堆。第一段可以比第二段少一點。

準備「英文作文」，可參考「學習出版公司」出版的：